KNOCK KNOCK JOKES & OTHER HILARIOUS GAGS

D0317655

AURA

This edition printed in 2015 by Baker & Taylor (UK) Ltd, Bicester, Oxfordshire, OX26 4ST

Licensed exclusively to Top That Publishing Ltd

Tide Mill Way, Woodbridge, Suffolk, IP12 1AP, UK

www.topthatpublishing.com

0 2 4 6 8 9 7 5 3 1

Manufactured in China

Knock Knock!
Who's there?
Dr.
Dr. Who?
You just said it!

Knock Knock!
Who's there?
Luke.
Luke who?
**Luke through
the keyhole and
find out!**

Knock Knock!
Who's there?
Ammonia.
Ammonia who?
**Ammonia little girl
and I can't reach
the door bell!**

Knock Knock!
Who's there?
Ice cream.
Ice cream who?
Ice cream loudly!

Knock Knock!
Who's there?
Heywood.
Heywood who?
Heywood you open the door!

Knock Knock!
Who's there?
Yah.
Yah who?
Are you a cowboy or something?

Knock Knock!
Who's there?
Lettuce.
Lettuce who?
Lettuce in!

Knock Knock!
Who's there?
Onya.
Onya who?
Onya marks, get set, go!

What do you call a guard with 100 legs?

A sentrypede!

What do cows like to dance to?

Any kind of moosic.

What books do chickens read?

Yolk books.

What's the best way to stop milk from going off?

Leaving it inside the cow.

Why was the centipede late?

Because he was playing 'This Little Piggy' with his baby brother!

What do you get if you cross a centipede and a chicken?

Enough drumsticks to feed an army!

What did one centipede say to the other centipede?

"You've got a lovely pair of legs, You've got a lovely pair of legs...!"

What did the earwig say as it fell down the stairs?

"Ear we go!"

Knock Knock!
Who's there?
Perry.
Perry who?
Perry well, thank you!

Knock Knock!
Who's there?
Summer.
Summer who?
Summer good, some are bad!

Knock Knock!
Who's there?
Ivana.
Ivana who?
Ivana be alone!

Knock Knock!
Who's there?
Carmen.
Carmen who?
Carmen get it!

Knock Knock!
Who's there?
Thumping.
Thumping who?
**Thumping green
and slimy just
crawled up
your leg!**

Knock Knock!
Who's there?
Ooze.
Ooze who?
**Ooze that knocking
on my door?**

Knock Knock!
Who's there?
Scott.
Scott who?
**Scott nothing to do
with you!**

Knock Knock!
Who's there?
Boo.
Boo who?
Don't cry!

Knock Knock!
Who's there?
Doris.
Doris who?
Doris locked, that's why I had to knock!

Knock Knock!
Who's there?
Toby.
Toby who?
Toby or not to be, that is the question!

Knock Knock!
Who's there?
Snow.
Snow who?
Snow good asking me!

Knock Knock!
Who's there?
Tank.
Tank who?
You're welcome!

Knock Knock!
Who's there?
Caesar.
Caesar who?
**Caesar jolly good
fellow!**

Knock Knock!
Who's there?
Keith.
Keith who?
**Keith me and
find out!**

Knock Knock!
Who's there?
Arthur.
Arthur who?
**Arthur moment
and I'll go round
the back!**

Knock Knock!
Who's there?
Olive.
Olive who?
Olive you!

Knock Knock!
Who's there?
Harry.
Harry who?
Harry up and open the door!

Knock Knock!
Who's there?
Anita.
Anita who?
Anita hug!

Knock Knock!
Who's there?
Oliver.
Oliver who?
Oliver across the road from you!

Knock Knock!
Who's there?
Hawaii.
Hawaii who?
I'm fine! Hawaii you?

Knock Knock!
Who's there?
Grandma. Knock knock!
Who's there?

Grandma. Knock Knock!
Who's there?
Grandma. Knock Knock!
Who's there?

Aunt.
Aunt who?
Aunt you glad Grandma's gone?

Knock Knock!
Who's there?
Ben.
Ben who?
**Ben wondering
what you're up to!**

Knock Knock!
Who's there?
**Control freak.
Now you say,
'control freak who?'**

Knock Knock!
Who's there?
Shelby.
Shelby who?
Shelby coming round the mountain when she comes!

Knock Knock!
Who's there?
Island.
Island who?
Island on Earth three days ago!

Knock Knock!
Who's there?
Woo.
Woo hoo?
Don't get so excited, it's just a joke!

Knock Knock!
Who's there?
Pecan.
Pecan who?
Pecan on someone your own size!

Knock Knock!
Who's there?
Gorilla.
Gorilla who?
Gorilla some cheese on toast please!

Knock Knock!
Who's there?
Aardvark.
Aardvark who?
Aardvark a million miles for one of your smiles!

Knock Knock!
Who's there?
Cows go.
Cows go who?
No! Cows go moo!

Knock Knock!
Who's there?
Annie.
Annie who?
Annie thing you can do I can do better!

Knock Knock!
Who's there?
Phyllis.
Phyllis who?
Phyllis up a glass of water!

Knock Knock!
Who's there?
Thistle.
Thistle who?
Thistle have to do until dinner's ready!

Knock Knock!
Who's there?
Police.
Police who?
Police stop telling these awful jokes!

Knock Knock!
Who's there?
Mary lee.
Mary lee who?
Mary lee we roll along!

Knock Knock!
Who's there?
Ray.
Ray who?
Ray-member me?

Knock Knock!
Who's there?
Plug.
Plug who?
Help, I'm going down the plug hole!

Knock Knock!
Who's there?
Hippo.
Hippo who?
Hippo birthday to you.
Hippo birthday to you!

Knock Knock!
Who's there?
Budgie.
Budgie who?
Budgie up, I want to squeeze in!

Knock Knock!
Who's there?
Ali.
Ali who?
Ali cat!

Knock Knock!
Who's there?
Andrew.
Andrew who?
Andrew all over the wall!

Knock Knock!
Who's there?
Repeat.
Repeat who?
Who who who!

Knock Knock!
Who's there?
Amos.
Amos who?
Amosquito bit me!

Knock Knock!
Who's there?
Janet.
Janet who?
Janet a big fish?

Knock Knock!
Who's there?
Nobel.
Nobel who?
**Nobel, that's
why I knocked!**

Knock Knock!
Who's there?
Sarah.
Sarah who?
**Sarah a doctor
in the house?**

Knock Knock!
Who's there?
Dot.
Dot who?
**Dot's for me to know
and you to find out!**

Knock Knock!
Who's there?
Turkey.
Turkey who?
Turkey to the right, then it'll open!

Knock Knock!
Who's there?
Moo.
Moo who?
Make up your mind, are you a cow or an owl?

Knock Knock!
Who's there?
Giraffe.
Giraffe who?
Giraffe anything to eat, I'm starving!

Knock Knock!
Who's there?
Bison.
Bison who?
Bison new handles, these don't work!

Knock Knock!
Who's there?
Theodore.
Theodore who?
**Theodore is stuck
and it won't open!**

Knock Knock!
Who's there?
Wilma.
Wilma who?
**Wilma supper
be ready soon?**

Knock Knock!
Who's there?
Cargo.
Cargo who?
Cargo beep beep!

Knock Knock!
Who's there?
Kanga.
Kanga who?
No Kangeroo!

Knock Knock!
Who's there?
Icon.
Icon who?
Icon tell you another knock knock joke. Do you want me to?

Knock Knock!
Who's there?
Despair.
Despair who?
Despair tyre is flat!

Knock Knock!
Who's there?
Vitamin.
Vitamin who?
Vitamin for a party!

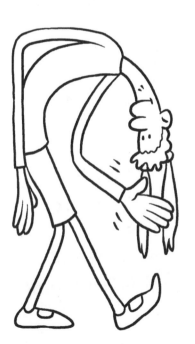

Knock Knock!
Who's there?
I used.
I used who?
I used to be able to reach the doorbell!

Knock Knock!
Who's there?
Hans!
Hans who?
Hans off my dog!

Knock Knock!
Who's there?
Claws!
Claws who?
Claws the door behind you!

Knock Knock!
Who's there?
Noise.
Noise who?
Noise to see you!

Knock Knock!
Who's there?
Neil.
Neil who?
Neil down and pet this cat!

What do you call a grasshopper with no legs?

A grasshover!

Why is it better to be a grasshopper than a cricket?

Because grasshoppers can play cricket, but crickets can't play grasshopper!

What's a teddy bear's favourite pasta?

Tagliateddy!

What is green and brown, has four legs and can kill you if it falls out of a tree and lands on you?

A bear on a branch.

What happened to the man who turned into an insect?

He just beetled off!

What is the insect's favourite game?

Cricket!

What's an insect's best chat-up line?

"Pardon me, but is this stool taken?"

What has four wheels and flies?

A rubbish bin!

Knock Knock!
Who's there?
Radio.
Radio who?
Radio not, here I come!

Knock Knock!
Who's there?
Omelette.
Omelette who?
Omelette smarter than you!

Knock Knock!
Who's there?
Justin.
Justin who?
Justin time for tea!

Knock Knock!
Who's there?
Maida.
Maida who?
Maida force be with you!

Knock Knock!
Who's there?
Egbert.
Egbert who?
Egbert no bacon, please!

Knock Knock!
Who's there?
Turnip.
Turnip who?
Turnip to school tomorrow or you'll be expelled!

Knock Knock!
Who's there?
Jess.
Jess who?
Jess me!

Knock Knock!
Who's there?
Ach.
Ach who?
Bless you!

Knock Knock!
Who's there?
Accordion.
Accordion who?
Accordion to the TV, it's going to rain tomorrow!

Knock Knock!
Who's there?
Ivor.
Ivor who?
Ivor message for you!

Knock Knock!
Who's there?
Wendy.
Wendy who?
Wendy wind blows the cradle will rock!

Knock Knock!
Who's there?
Soup.
Soup who?
Souperman!

Knock Knock!
Who's there?
Value.
Value who?
Value be my Valentine?

Knock Knock!
Who's there?
Abbey.
Abbey who?
Abbey stung me on the nose!

Knock Knock!
Who's there?
Shirley.
Shirley who?
Shirley you know my name by now!

Knock Knock!
Who's there?
Wales.
Wales who?
Wales as long as I'm here, let's go out!

Knock Knock!
Who's there?
Butter.
Butter who?
I butter not tell you!

Knock Knock!
Who's there?
Rotten egg.
Rotten egg who?
**Splat! The yolks
on you!**

Knock Knock!
Who's there?
Red Denny.
Red Denny who?
**Red Denny good
books lately?**

Knock Knock!
Who's there?
Wanda.
Wanda who?
**Wanda know, then
open the door!**

Knock Knock!
Who's there?
Sacha.
Sacha who?
Sacha fuss because I knocked on your door!

Knock Knock!
Who's there?
Isabelle.
Isabelle who?
Isabelle necessary on your door?

Knock Knock!
Who's there?
Wayne.
Wayne who?
Wayne, wayne go away, come again another day!

Knock Knock!
Who's there?
Safari.
Safari who?
Safari so good!

Knock Knock!
Who's there?
P.
P who?
Well, thanks for telling me I smell!

Knock Knock!
Who's there?
Bow.
Bow who?
Not bow who, bow wow!

Knock Knock!
Who's there?
Orange.
Orange who?
Orange you going to open the door?

Knock Knock!
Who's there?
Flea.
Flea who?
Flea from that dog before he bites you!

Knock Knock!
Who's there?
Igloo.
Igloo who?
Igloo knew Steven like I knew Steven!

Knock Knock!
Who's there?
Mister.
Mister who?
Mister last train!

Knock Knock!
Who's there?
Water.
Water who?
Water you doing in my house!

Knock Knock!
Who's there?
Pooch.
Pooch who?
Pooch your arms around me!

Knock Knock!
Who's there?
Nanna.
Nanna who?
**Nanna your
business!**

Knock Knock!
Who's there?
Witches.
Witches who?
**Witches the way
home?**

Knock Knock!
Who's there?
Ralph.
Ralph who?
**Ralph! Ralph!
Ralph! I'm a dog!**

Knock Knock!
Who's there?
Pig.
Pig who?
**Pig up your feet or
you'll trip up!**

Knock Knock!
Who's there?
Celia.
Celia who?
Celia later alligator, don't forget your toilet paper!

Knock Knock!
Who's there?
Saffron.
Saffron who?
Saffron a chair and it collapsed!

Knock Knock!
Who's there?
Larva.
Larva who?
Larva cup of tea!

Knock Knock!
Who's there?
Wooden shoe.
Wooden shoe who?
Wooden shoe like to know!

Knock Knock!
Who's there?
Harley.
Harley who?
Harley see you anymore!

Knock Knock!
Who's there?
Ray.
Ray who?
Ray-ning cats and dogs!

Knock Knock!
Who's there?
Ida.
Ida who?
Ida know, sorry!

Knock Knock!
Who's there?
Wade.
Wade who?
Wade till next time!

Knock Knock!
Who's there?
Alvin.
Alvin who?
Alvin a great time, how about you?

Knock Knock!
Who's there?
Haden.
Haden who?
Haden seek!

Knock Knock!
Who's there?
Galway.
Galway who?
Galway, you bother me!

Knock Knock!
Who's there?
Waiter.
Waiter who?
Waiter minute while I tie my shoe!

Knock Knock!
Who's there?
Figs.
Figs who?
Figs the doorbell because it's broken!

Knock Knock!
Who's there?
Handsome.
Handsome who?
Handsome of that pizza to me!

Knock Knock!
Who's there?
Isadore.
Isadore who?
Isadore always that hard to knock on?

Knock Knock!
Who's there?
Wine.
Wine who?
Wine don't you like these jokes?

Knock Knock!
Who's there?
Avocado.
Avocado who?
Avocado cold!

Knock Knock!
Who's there?
Eyesore!
Eyesore who?
Eyesore do like you!

Knock Knock!
Who's there?
Candace.
Candace who?
Candace be the last knock knock joke?

Knock Knock!
Who's there?
Sam.
Sam who?
Sam person who knocked on the door last time!

Knock Knock!
Who's there?
Venice.
Venice who?
Venice your mother coming home?

Knock Knock!
Who's there?
Al.
Al who?
Al give you a kiss if you open the door!

Knock Knock!
Who's there?
Alfie.
Alfie who?
Alfie terrible if you leave!

Knock Knock!
Who's there?
Canoe.
Canoe who?
Canoe lend me some money?

Knock Knock!
Who's there?
Waddle.
Waddle who?
**Waddle you give me
if I go away?**

Knock Knock!
Who's there?
Lass.
Lass who?
**That's what cowboys
do, isn't it?**

Knock Knock!
Who's there?
Ike.
Ike who?
**Ike can't stop
laughing!**

Knock Knock!
Who's there?
Thermos.
Thermos who?
**Thermos be a better
joke than this!**

What dog wears contact lenses?

A cock-eyed spaniel!

What is a dog's favourite flower?

Anything in your garden!

What's a dog's favourite hobby?

Collecting fleas!

How many seasons are there in a dog's life?

Just one, the moulting season!

Why is it called a 'litter' of puppies?

Because they mess up the whole house!

How do you stop a dog smelling?

Put a peg on its nose!

What is the best time to take a rottweiler for a walk?

Any time he wants to!

When does a dog go 'moo'?

When it is learning a new language!

Knock Knock!
Who's there?
Alfred.
Alfred who?
**Alfred the needle
if you sew!**

Knock Knock!
Who's there?
Aesop.
Aesop who?
**Aesop I saw a
puddy cat!**

Knock Knock!
Who's there?
Alec.
Alec who?
Alec my lolly!

Knock Knock!
Who's there?
Veal chop.
Veal chop who?
**Veal chop around and
see what bargains
we can find!**

Knock Knock!
Who's there?
Foster.
Foster who?
Foster than a speeding bullet!

Knock Knock!
Who's there?
Haden!
Haden who?
Haden in the bushes!

Knock Knock!
Who's there?
Sabina!
Sabina who?
Sabina long time since I saw you!

Knock Knock!
Who's there?
Sara.
Sara who?
Sara no other way into this building?

Knock Knock!
Who's there?
Eamon.
Eamon who?
Eamon a good mood today, thank you!

Knock Knock!
Who's there?
Sherwood.
Sherwood who?
Sherwood like to meet you!

Knock Knock!
Who's there?
Boliva.
Boliva who?
Boliva me I know what I'm talking about!

Knock Knock!
Who's there?
Zookeeper.
Zookeeper who?
Zookeeper away from him!

Knock Knock!
Who's there?
Ester.
Ester who?
Ester anything I can do for you?

Knock Knock!
Who's there?
Eve.
Eve who?
Eve ho me hearties!

Knock Knock!
Who's there?
Abbott.
Abbott who?
Abbott time you opened the door!

Knock Knock!
Who's there?
Watson.
Watson who?
Watson television?

Knock Knock!
Who's there?
Zizi.
Zizi who?
Zizi when you know how!

Knock Knock!
Who's there?
Tennessee.
Tennessee who?
Tennessee you later!

Knock Knock!
Who's there?
Julia.
Julia who?
Julia want some cookies?

Knock Knock!
Who's there?
Budda.
Budda who?
Budda this slice of bread for me!

Knock Knock!
Who's there?
Reed.
Reed who?
**Reed-turn to sender,
address unknown!**

Knock Knock!
Who's there?
Weasel.
Weasel who?
**Weasel while
you work!**

Knock Knock!
Who's there?
Daisy.
Daisy who?
**Daisy said you
were in but I
don't believe them!**

Knock Knock!
Who's there?
Lisa.
Lisa who?
**Lisa you can do
is let me in!**

Knock Knock!
Who's there?
Jamie.
Jamie who?
Jamie'n you don't recognise my voice?

Knock Knock!
Who's there?
Catsup.
Catsup who?
Catsup a tree and she won't come down!

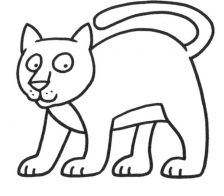

Knock Knock!
Who's there?
Cash.
Cash who?
I knew you were nuts!

Knock Knock!
Who's there?
Closure.
Closure who?
Closure mouth when you're eating!

Knock Knock!
Who's there?
Len.
Len who?
Len me a fiver!

Knock Knock!
Who's there?
L.A.
L.A. who?
L.A. down for a snooze and slept all afternoon!

Knock Knock!
Who's there?
Mind.
Mind who?
Mind your own business!

Knock Knock!
Who's there?
Dishwasher.
Dishwasher who?
Dishwasher way I talked before I got my new teeth!

Knock Knock!
Who's there?
Mark.
Mark who?
Mark your calendar, my birthday's soon!

Knock Knock!
Who's there?
Jimmy.
Jimmy who?
Jimmy some cake I'm starving!

Knock Knock!
Who's there?
Chuck.
Chuck who?
Chuck-olate bunny!

Knock Knock!
Who's there?
Witch.
Witch who?
Witch you stop asking and open the door?

Knock Knock!
Who's there?
Howard.
Howard who?
Howard you like to go out today?

Knock Knock!
Who's there?
Ivan.
Ivan who?
Ivan headache!

Knock Knock!
Who's there?
Button.
Button who?
Button in is not polite!

Knock Knock!
Who's there?
Eustace.
Eustace who?
Come Eustace you are!

What do you call a flea that lives in an idiot's ear?

A space invader!

What do you get if you cross a rabbit and a flea?

Bugs Bunny!

How do you start an insect race?

One, two, flea – go!

Where do fleas live?

Fleadelphia!

What is the difference between a flea and a wolf?

One prowls on the hairy and the other howls on the prairie!

How do you find where a flea has bitten you?

Start from scratch!

What do you call a Russian flea?

A Moscow-ito!

Knock Knock!
Who's there?
Duck.
Duck who?
Just duck!
They're throwing
things at us!

Knock Knock!
Who's there?
Hoo.
Hoo who?
Is there an owl
in here?

Knock Knock!
Who's there?
Lion.
Lion who?
Lion on your
doorstep, open up!

Knock Knock!
Who's there?
Argue.
Argue who?
Argue going to
let me in or not?

Knock Knock!
Who's there?
Mae.
Mae who?
**Mae be I'll tell you
and maybe I won't!**

Knock Knock!
Who's there?
Cauliflower.
Cauliflower who?
**Cauliflower by any
other name and it's
still a daisy!**

Knock Knock!
Who's there?
Alec.
Alec who?
**Alec-tricity. Isn't
that a shock!**

Knock Knock!
Who's there?
Bacon.
Bacon who?
**Bacon a cake for
your birthday!**

What did the dog do with the history professor?

They got together and talked over old times.

What did the dog get when he multiplied 497 by 684?

The wrong answer.

What did the dog say to the candle?

"Are you going out tonight?"

What did the dog say to the pig?

"You are just a bore."

What did the dog say when he chased his tail?

"This is the end."

What did the dog take when he was run down?

The license number of the car that hit him.

What did the dog tell his owner when he saw the dog-catcher coming?

Nothing. Dogs don't talk.

What does a dog become after it is six years old?

Seven years old.

What do
bees chew?

Bumble gum!

What does a cat
go to sleep on?

A caterpillow!

Why are As like
flowers?

Because Bs come
after them!

What does a
caterpillar do on
New Year's Day?

Turns over a
new leaf!

What is the definition of a caterpillar?

A worm in a fur coat!

What has stripes and pulls a tractor?

A caterpillar tractor!

What is worse than a giraffe with a sore throat?

A centipede with chilblains!

What has 50 legs but can't walk?

Half a centipede!

What do angry spiders do?

They go up the wall.

Two fleas were running across the top of a cereal packet.

"Why are we running so fast?" asked one.

"Because it says 'tear along the dotted line'!"

What is the most faithful insect?

A flea – once they find someone they like, they stick to them!

What do you call a cheerful flea?

A hop-timist!

What did the romantic flea say?

"I love you aw-flea!"

Why is a polar bear a cheap pet?

It lives on ice!

How do you keep flies out of the kitchen?

Put a pile of manure in the living room!

What is the difference between a fly and a bird?

A bird can fly but a fly can't bird!

Knock Knock!
Who's there?
Norway.
Norway who?
Norway will I leave until you open this door!

Knock Knock!
Who's there?
Ina.
Ina who?
Ina minute I'm going to knock this door down!

Knock Knock!
Who's there?
Banana.
Banana who?
Banana split so ice creamed!

Knock Knock!
Who's there?
Robin.
Robin who?
Robin the bank!

Knock Knock!
Who's there?
Alaska.
Alaska who?
**Alaska my friend
the question!**

Knock Knock!
Who's there?
Pudding.
Pudding who?
**Pudding your shoes
on before your
trousers is stupid!**

Knock Knock!
Who's there?
Steve.
Steve who?
Steve upper lip!

Knock Knock!
Who's there?
Europe.
Europe who?
**Europe'ning the door
too slowly! Come on!**

Knock Knock!
Who's there?
Candy.
Candy who?
Candy cow jump over the moon?

Knock Knock!
Who's there?
Cheese.
Cheese who?
Cheese to meet you!

Knock Knock!
Who's there?
Iguana.
Iguana who?
Iguana hold your hand!

Knock Knock!
Who's there?
Gary.
Gary who?
Gary on typing!

Knock Knock!
Who's there?
Aida.
Aida who?
Aida lot of sweets and now my tummy aches!

Knock Knock!
Who's there?
Kay.
Kay who?
K, L, M, N, O, P, Q, R, S, T, U, V, W, X, Y, Z!

Knock Knock!
Who's there?
I don't know.
I don't know who?
I don't know. Why don't you believe me?

Knock Knock!
Who's there?
Adair.
Adair who?
Adair hair but now I'm bald.

66

What did the angry man sing when he found his slippers chewed up by the new puppy?

"I must throw that doggie out the window!"

Why do dogs wag their tails?

Because no-one else will do it for them!

What happened to the dog that ate nothing but garlic?

His bark was much worse than his bite!

Why do dogs bury bones in the ground?

Because you can't bury them in trees!

What happened when the dog went to the flea circus?

He stole the show!

How do you know if you have a stupid dog?

It chases parked cars!

What do you get if you cross a dog with concorde?

A jet setter!

Why did the dog wear white sneakers?

Because his boots were at the menders!

Knock Knock!
Who's there?
Blue.
Blue who?
Blue away with the wind!

Knock Knock!
Who's there?
Keanu.
Keanu who?
Keanu let me in, it's cold out here!

Knock Knock!
Who's there?
Termite.
Termite who?
Termite's the night!

Knock Knock!
Who's there?
Ivan.
Ivan who?
Ivan new hat. Do you like it?

Knock Knock!
Who's there?
Yule.
Yule who.
Yule never know!

Knock Knock!
Who's there?
Samuel.
Samuel who?
Samuel you'll be famous one day!

Knock Knock!
Who's there?
Rhoda.
Rhoda who?
Row row rhoda boat ...

Knock Knock!
Who's there?
Abba.
Abba who?
Abba-out turn!
Quick march!

What did the dog use to make his kite?

Flypaper.

What dog can jump higher than a tree?

Any dog can jump higher than a tree. Trees don't jump.

What eats dog food, lives in a doghouse and is very dangerous?

A dog with a machine gun.

What pill would you give to an elephant that can't sleep?

Trunkquilizers!

What do you call a three-legged donkey?

A wonkey.

What's the difference between an elephant and a gooseberry?

A gooseberry is green!

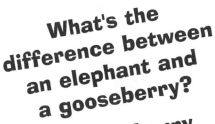

A boy with an elephant on his head went to see a doctor. The doctor said, "You know, you really need help."

"Yes I do," said the elephant, "get this kid off my foot!"

Why do elephants have trunks?

Because they would look silly carrying suitcases!

Knock Knock!
Who's there?
Uganda.
Uganda who?
Uganda get away with this!

Knock Knock!
Who's there?
Leaf.
Leaf who?
Leaf me alone!

Knock Knock!
Who's there?
You.
You who?
You who, is anybody in?

Knock Knock!
Who's there?
Quacker.
Quacker who?
Quacker another bad joke and I'm leaving!

Knock Knock!
Who's there?
Farmer.
Farmer who?
Farmer birthday I'm getting a new bike!

Knock Knock!
Who's there?
Rabbit.
Rabbit who?
Rabbit up carefully, it's a present!

Knock Knock!
Who's there?
Sherlock.
Sherlock who?
Sherlock your back door, someone will break in!

Knock Knock!
Who's there?
Norma Lee.
Norma Lee who?
Norma Lee I have my key!

What kind of meat do you give a stupid dog?

Chump chops!

What sort of clothes does a pet dog wear?

A petticoat!

What do you get if you cross a sheepdog with a rose?

A collie-flower!

Why did the dachshund bite the woman's ankle?

Because he was short and couldn't reach any higher!

Why did the snowman call his dog Frost?

Because frost bites!

Why did the poor dog chase his own tail?

He was trying to make both ends meet!

Where does a rottweiler sit in the cinema?

Anywhere it wants to!

What does a lion brush his mane with?

A catacomb!

Knock Knock!
Who's there?
Camilla.
Camilla who?
Camilla minute!

Knock Knock!
Who's there?
A Fred.
A Fred who?
Whose a Fred of the Big, Bad Wolf?

Knock Knock!
Who's there?
Yolanda.
Yolanda who?
Yolanda some money?

Knock Knock!
Who's there?
Madrid.
Madrid who?
Madrid you wash my jeans?

Knock Knock!
Who's there?
Teddy.
Teddy who?
**Teddy is the beginning
of the rest of your life!**

Knock Knock!
Who's there?
Bless.
Bless who?
I didn't sneeze!

Knock Knock!
Who's there?
Alex.
Alex who?
Alex plain later!

Knock Knock!
Who's there?
Almond.
Almond who?
**Almond the side
of the law!**

What do polar bears have for lunch?

Ice burgers.

What goes hum-choo, hum-choo?

A bee with a cold.

What's a bee-line?

The shortest distance between two buzz-stops!

What is the difference between an elephant and a flea?

An elephant can have fleas but a flea can't have elephants!

Why do bees hum?

Because they've forgotten the words!

Why did the elephant paint his toenails red?

So he could hide in the cherry tree!

What do you call an elephant that flies?

A jumbo jet!

How do you know when there is an elephant under your bed?

When your nose touches the ceiling!

What bee is good for your health?

Vitamin bee!

What is black and yellow and buzzes along at 30,000 feet?

A bee in an aeroplane!

What does a bee say before it stings you?

"This is going to hurt me a lot more than it hurts you!"

Who are the cleverest bees?

Spelling bees!

81

Why did the queen bee kick out all of the other bees?

Because they kept droning on and on!

How many bees do you need in a bee choir?

A humdred!

What pillar doesn't need holding up?

A caterpillar!

What kind of bee can keep an aeroplane dry?

An aero-drone!

Knock Knock!
Who's there?
Vaughn.
Vaughn who?
Vaughn day my prince will come!

Knock Knock!
Who's there?
Violet.
Violet who?
Violet the cat out of the bag?

Knock Knock!
Who's there?
Truffle.
Truffle who?
Truffle with you is that you're too shy!

Knock Knock!
Who's there?
Nadia.
Nadia who?
Just Nadia head if you understand!

Knock Knock!
Who's there?
Imogen.
Imogen who?
Imogen life without chocolate!

83

Knock Knock!
Who's there?
Wanda.
Wanda who?
Wanda get some cake?

Knock Knock!
Who's there?
Lionel.
Lionel who?
Lionel get you nowhere, tell the truth!

Knock Knock!
Who's there?
Bach.
Bach who?
Bach to work you slackers!

84

Knock Knock!
Who's there?
Ray.
Ray who?
Ray-ning cats and dogs!

Knock Knock!
Who's there?
Ear.
Ear who?
Ear you are, I've been looking for you!

Knock Knock!
Who's there?
Humphrey.
Humphrey who?
Hum three notes and I'll name that tune!

Knock Knock!
Who's there?
Peek Ash.
Peek Ash who?
Pikachu, I choose you!

Knock Knock!
Who's there?
Avenue.
Avenue who?
Avenue heard this joke before?

Knock Knock!
Who's there?
Window.
Window who?
Window I get my dinner?

Knock Knock!
Who's there?
Senior.
Senior who?
Senior so nosey, I'm not going to tell you!

Knock Knock!
Who's there?
Disease.
Disease who?
Disease trousers fit you?

What does a spider do when he gets angry?

He goes up the wall!

Why are spiders good swimmers?

They have webbed feet!

What do you get if you cross a skunk with a teddy bear?

Winnie the Pooh.

What do you call a bee who's had a spell put on him?

Bee-witched!

Can bees fly
in the rain?

Not without
their little yellow
jackets!

What buzzes,
is black and yellow
and goes along
the bottom
of the sea?

A bee in a
submarine!

What's a lion's
favourite food?

Baked beings!

What would happen
if tarantulas were as
big as horses?

If one bit you, you
could ride it to
hospital!

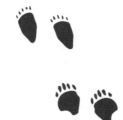

Knock Knock!
Who's there?
Iam.
Iam who?
Sorry I don't know who you are!

Knock Knock!
Who's there?
Letter.
Letter who?
Letter keep knocking!

Knock Knock!
Who's there?
Alpaca.
Alpaca who?
Alpaca lunch, let's go for a picnic!

Knock Knock!
Who's there?
Tom Sawyer.
Tom Sawyer who?
Tom sawyer underwear!

Knock Knock!
Who's there?
Utah.
Utah who?
You talking to me?

Knock Knock!
Who's there?
Oscar.
Oscar who?
**Oscar stupid
question, you get
a stupid answer!**

Knock Knock!
Who's there?
Sherwood.
Sherwood who?
**Sure would like you
to open the door!**

Knock Knock!
Who's there?
Mike.
Mike who?
**My cup is empty.
Can I have a refill?**

Knock Knock!
Who's there?
Wanda.
Wanda who?
Wanda where I put my car keys?

Knock Knock!
Who's there?
Jamaica.
Jamaica who?
Jamaica good grade on the test?

Knock Knock!
Who's there?
Carrot.
Carrot who?
Do you carrot all about me?

Knock Knock!
Who's there?
Wooden.
Wooden who?
Wooden you like to know!

Knock Knock!
Who's there?
Stan.
Stan who?
Stan back, I think I'm going to sneeze!

Knock Knock!
Who's there?
Conrad.
Conrad who?
Conradulations, I used your joke!

Knock Knock!
Who's there?
Distressing.
Distressing who?
Distressing has too much vinegar!

Knock Knock!
Who's there?
Ewe.
Ewe who?
Who me? What do you want?

Why did the fly fly?

Because the spider spied her.

What has six legs, bites and talks in code?

A morse-quito!

What's pretty, delicate and carries a sub-machine-gun?

A killer butterfly!

How do you make a butter-fly?

Flick it out of the butter dish with a knife!

What insect lives on nothing?

A moth, because it eats holes.

What do insects learn at school?

Mothmatics!

What do you get if you cross a firefly and a moth?

An insect who can find its way around a dark wardrobe!

How do stones stop moths eating your clothes?

Because rolling stones gather no moths!

Knock Knock!
Who's there?
Italian.
Italian who?
Italian you for the last time, open the door!

Knock Knock!
Who's there?
Justin.
Justin who?
Justin the neighbourhood, thought I'd come by!

Knock Knock!
Who's there?
Your mum.
Your mum who?
You don't know who your mum is?

Knock Knock!
Who's there?
Sarah.
Sarah who?
Sarah reason you're not laughing?

Knock Knock!
Who's there?
Howard.
Howard who?
Howard your maths test go today?

Knock Knock!
Who's there?
Claire.
Claire who?
Claire the way, I'm coming in!

Knock Knock!
Who's there?
General Lee.
General Lee who?
General Lee I do not tell jokes!

Knock Knock!
Who's there?
House.
House who?
House it going?

Knock Knock!
Who's there?
Colleen.
Colleen who?
Colleen up your room – it's a mess!

Knock Knock!
Who's there?
Emma.
Emma who?
Emma cracking you up?

Knock Knock!
Who's there?
Kip.
Kip who?
Kip your hands off me!

Knock Knock!
Who's there?
Vida.
Vida who?
Vida you talk like that?

Knock Knock!
Who's there?
Rufus.
Rufus who?
Your rufus on fire!

Knock Knock!
Who's there?
Warren.
Warren who?
Warren peace is a famous Russian novel!

Knock Knock!
Who's there?
Hoffman.
Hoffman who?
I'll Hoffman, I'll puff, and I'll blow your house down!

Knock Knock!
Who's there?
Luke.
Luke who?
Luke out! Here comes another knock knock joke!

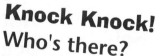

Knock Knock!
Who's there?
Linnekar.
Linnekar who?
Linnekars in a big traffic jam!

Knock Knock!
Who's there?
Champ.
Champ who?
Champ poo your hair, it's dirty!

Knock Knock!
Who's there?
Holdon.
Holdon who?
Holdon I'll go see!

Knock Knock!
Who's there?
I Love.
I Love who?
I don't know, who do you love?

Knock Knock!
Who's there?
Anna.
Anna who?
Anna body know some more jokes?

Knock Knock!
Who's there?
Dewey.
Dewey who?
Dewey have to listen to all this knocking?

Knock Knock!
Who's there?
Easter.
Easter who?
Easter bunny!

Knock Knock!
Who's there?
Anna.
Anna who?
Anna nother Easter bunny!

Knock Knock!
Who's there?
Max.
Max who?
Max no difference!

Knock Knock!
Who's there?
Dishes.
Dishes who?
Dishes me.
Who is this?

Knock Knock!
Who's there?
Ketchup.
Ketchup who?
Ketchup to me
and I'll tell you!

Knock Knock!
Who's there?
Madam.
Madam who?
Madam finger is
stuck in the door!

Knock Knock!
Who's there?
Daisy.
Daisy who?
Daisy plays, night he sleeps!

Knock Knock!
Who's there?
Doris.
Doris who?
Doris open, come on in!

Knock Knock!
Who's there?
Little old lady.
Little old lady who?
I didn't know you could yodel!

Knock Knock!
Who's there?
Aware.
Aware who?
Aware oh where have my little sheep gone?

Knock Knock!
Who's there?
Omelette.
Omelette who?
Omelette smarter than I look!

Knock Knock!
Who's there?
Spider.
Spider who?
You tried to hide her, but I spider!

Knock Knock!
Who's there?
Goat.
Goat who?
Goat to the door and find out!

Knock Knock!
Who's there?
Dexter.
Dexter who?
Dexter hall with boughs of holly!

Knock Knock!
Who's there?
Ilona.
Ilona who?
Ilona Ranger!

Knock Knock!
Who's there?
Labrador.
Labrador who?
Labrador is a city, not a person!

Knock Knock!
Who's there?
Arthur.
Arthur who?
Arthur anymore home like you?

Knock Knock!
Who's there?
Warrior.
Warrior who?
Warrior been all my life?

Knock Knock!
Who's there?
Avon.
Avon who?
Avon to be alone!

Knock Knock!
Who's there?
Butcher.
Butcher who?
**Butcher arms
around me!**

Knock Knock!
Who's there?
Abyssinia.
Abyssinia who?
Abyssinia soon!

Knock Knock!
Who's there?
Major.
Major who?
**Major open the
door, didn't I?**

Knock Knock!
Who's there?
Manny.
Manny who?
**Manny are called,
but few are chosen!**

Knock Knock!
Who's there?
Donna.
Donna who?
**Donna sit under
the apple tree?**

Knock Knock!
Who's there?
Sony.
Sony who?
Sony a paper moon!

Knock Knock!
Who's there?
Doughnut.
Doughnut who?
**Doughnut ask me
that silly question!**

Knock Knock!
Who's there?
Elsie.
Elsie who?
**Elsie you in my
dreams!**

Knock Knock!
Who's there?
Dwayne.
Dwayne who?
**Dwayne the
swimming pool,
it's full of bugs!**

Knock Knock!
Who's there?
Pizza.
Pizza who?
**Pizza on Earth and
goodwill to all men!**

Knock Knock!
Who's there?
Lil.
Lil who?
**Lil things count
the most!**

Knock Knock!
Who's there?
Frank and Stan.
Frank and Stan who?
**Frankenstein the
monster!**

Knock Knock!
Who's there?
Athea.
Athea who?
Athea later alligator!

Knock Knock!
Who's there?
Andy.
Andy who?
**Andy that he has
to give me all his
sweets!**

Knock Knock!
Who's there?
Myth.
Myth who?
Myth you too!

Knock Knock!
Who's there?
Alison.
Alison who?
Alison to my radio in the morning!

Knock Knock!
Who's there?
Kent.
Kent who?
Kent you tell?

Knock Knock!
Who's there?
Sabina.
Sabina who?
Sabina long time since I saw you!

Knock Knock!
Who's there?
Olive.
Olive who?
Olive here, now let me in!

Knock Knock!
Who's there?
Wooden shoe.
Wooden shoe who?
**Wooden shoe like
to know!**

Knock Knock!
Who's there?
Felix.
Felix who?
**Felix my ice-cream
again, I'll bash him!**

Knock Knock!
Who's there?
Snow.
Snow who?
**Snow use, I've
forgotten my
name again!**

Knock Knock!
Who's there?
Canoe.
Canoe who?
**Canoe help me with my
homework, please?**

Knock Knock!
Who's there?
Alba.
Alba who?
Alba in the kitchen if you need me!

Knock Knock!
Who's there?
Frank.
Frank who?
Frank you for being my friend!

Knock Knock!
Who's there?
Aladdin.
Aladdin who?
Aladdin the street wants a word with you!

Knock Knock!
Who's there?
Interrupting cow.
Interrupti-
Mooooooo!

Knock Knock!
Who's there?
Alex.
Alex who?
Alex the questions around here!

Knock Knock!
Who's there?
Carl.
Carl who?
Carl get you there quicker than walking!

Knock Knock!
Who's there?
De Niro.
De Niro who?
De Niro I am to you the more I like you!

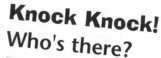

Knock Knock!
Who's there?
Nuisance.
Nuisance who?
What's nuisance yesterday?

Knock Knock!
Who's there?
Haiti.
Haiti who?
Haiti see good food go to waste!

Knock Knock!
Who's there?
Tyson.
Tyson who?
Tyson of this on for size!

Knock Knock!
Who's there?
India.
India who?
India night time I go to sleep!

Knock Knock!
Who's there?
Andy.
Andy who?
Andy bit me again!

Knock Knock!
Who's there?
Broccoli.
Broccoli who?
Broccoli doesn't have a second name!

Knock Knock!
Who's there?
Apple.
Apple who?
Apple your hair if you don't let me in!

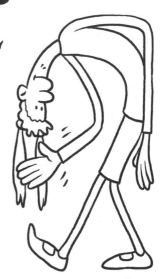

Knock Knock!
Who's there?
Cheese.
Cheese who?
Cheese a good girl!

Knock Knock!
Who's there?
Berlin.
Berlin who?
Berlin the water to cook an egg!

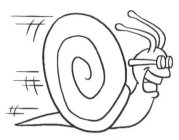

Knock Knock!
Who's there?
Insect.
Insect who?
**Insect your
name here!**

Knock Knock!
Who's there?
Pickle.
Pickle who?
**Oh, that's my favourite
instrument!**

Knock Knock!
Who's there?
Read.
Read who?
**Read between
the lines!**

Knock Knock!
Who's there?
Ice cream soda.
Ice cream soda who?
**Ice cream soda
whole world knows
what a nut you are!**

Knock Knock!
Who's there?
A herd.
A herd who?
A herd you were home so I came over!

Knock Knock!
Who's there?
No one.
No one who?
NO ONE!

Knock Knock!
Who's there?
Ivor.
Ivor who?
Ivor you let me in or I climb through the window!

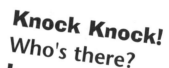

Knock Knock!
Who's there?
Officer O'Brian.
Officer O'Brian who?
Officer O'Brian from the police station!

116

Knock Knock!
Who's there?
Norman.
Norman who?
Norman invasion 1066!

Knock Knock!
Who's there?
Maggot?
Maggot who?
Maggot me this new shirt today!

Knock Knock!
Who's there?
I've done up.
I've done up who?
Ha Ha Ha Ha!

Knock Knock!
Who's there?
Dismay.
Dismay who?
Dismay be a joke but it's not funny!

Knock Knock!
Who's there?
July.
July who?
July or you tell the truth?

117

Knock Knock!
Who's there?
Amanda.
Amanda who?
Amanda doctor's orders at the moment!

Knock Knock!
Who's there?
Ewan.
Ewan who?
Ewan me are supposed to go out today!

Knock Knock!
Who's there?
Ida.
Ida who?
Ida awful day today!

118

Knock Knock!
Who's there?
Theo.
Theo who?
The cinema is showing a good film tonight. Do you want to go?

Knock Knock!
Who's there?
Justin.
Justin who?
Justin time I found you!

Knock Knock!
Who's there?
Sandy.
Sandy who?
Sandy shore!

Knock Knock!
Who's there?
Mabel.
Mabel who?
Mabel isn't working either!

Knock Knock!
Who's there?
Kermit.
Kermit who?
**Kermit a crime
and you go to jail!**

Knock Knock!
Who's there?
Mary.
Mary who?
**Mary Christmas
everyone!**

Knock Knock!
Who's there?
Lydia.
Lydia who?
Lydia dustbin is loose!

Knock Knock!
Who's there?
Norma.
Norma who?
**Normally the butler
opens the door!**

Knock Knock!
Who's there?
Amanda.
Amanda who?
Amanda the table!

Knock Knock!
Who's there?
Innuendo.
Innuendo who?
Innuendo the dinner you get dessert!

Knock Knock!
Who's there?
Pear.
Pear who?
Pear of shoes!

Knock Knock!
Who's there?
Wicked.
Wicked who?
Wicked make music together!

Knock Knock!
Who's there?
Bella.
Bella who?
Bella the ball!

Knock Knock!
Who's there?
Perry.
Perry who?
**Perry well,
thank you!**

Knock Knock!
Who's there?
Micky.
Micky who?
**Micky won't fit in the
lock – that's why I'm
knocking!**

Knock Knock!
Who's there?
Dummy.
Dummy who?
Dummy a favour and let me in!

What is the difference between Father Christmas and a warm dog?

Father Christmas wears a whole suit, a dog just pants!

How can you get a set of teeth put in for free?

Hit a lion!

When is the most likely time that a stray dog will walk into your house?

When the door is open!

What do you get if you cross a dog and a cheetah?

A dog that chases cars – and catches them!

What happens when it rains cats and dogs?

You can step in a poodle!

What kind of dog sounds like you can eat it?

A sausage dog!

What goes 99-clonk, 99-clonk, 99-clonk?

A centipede with a wooden leg!

What is worse than an alligator with toothache?

A centipede with athlete's foot!

What do you get if you cross a centipede and a parrot?

A walkie talkie!

What do you do if your dog eats your pen?

Use a pencil instead!

Why don't dogs make good dancers?

Because they have two left feet!

What do you get if you cross a rottweiler and a hyena?

I don't know, but I'll join in if it laughs!

What do dogs have that no other animal has?

Puppy dogs!

What do you call a fake noodle?

An impasta!

What is a dog's favourite sport?

Formula One drooling!

What is a dog's favourite food?

Anything that is on your plate!

Knock Knock!
Who's there?
Cat.
Cat who?
Caterpillar!

Knock Knock!
Who's there?
Yula.
Yula who?
Yula apologise for not letting me in sooner!

Knock Knock!
Who's there?
Alec.
Alec who?
Alec Jack, but I don't like you!

Knock Knock!
Who's there?
White.
White who?
White in the middle!

Knock Knock!
Who's there?
Money.
Money who?
Money is stiff, I hurt it playing football!

Knock Knock!
Who's there?
Major.
Major who?
Major answer, didn't I!

Knock Knock!
Who's there?
CDs.
CDs who?
CDs fingers? They're freezing! Let me in!

Knock Knock!
Who's there?
Ivan.
Ivan who?
Ivan infectious disease!

Knock Knock!
Who's there?
Who stole?
Who stole who?
Who stole what, and I'll tell you if you let me!

Knock Knock!
Who's there?
Judo.
Judo who?
What, Judo know?

Knock Knock!
Who's there?
Imago.
Imago who?
Imago ahead and tell you!

Knock Knock!
Who's there?
Owl.
Owl who?
Owl you know unless you open the door?

Knock Knock!
Who's there?
Jack.
Jack who?
**Jack be nimble,
Jack be quick!**

Knock Knock!
Who's there?
Kook.
Kook who?
**Do you know, you
have a real future
in Swiss clocks!**

Knock Knock!
Who's there?
Archibald.
Archibald who?
**Archibald on top
of your head!**

Knock Knock!
Who's there?
Paul Aidy.
Paul Aidy who?
**Paul Aidy, she
tripped and fell over!**

Knock Knock!
Who's there?
Tim.
Tim who?
Timber!

Knock Knock!
Who's there?
Cockadoodle.
Cockadoodle who?
No! Cockadoodle doo!

Knock Knock!
Who's there?
Tail.
Tail who?
**Tail all your
friends this joke!**

Knock Knock!
Who's there?
William.
William who?
William mind your own business!

Knock Knock!
Who's there?
House.
House who?
House soon do you want to hear this joke?

Knock Knock!
Who's there?
Otto.
Otto who?
Otto know I can't remember!

Knock Knock!
Who's there?
Erma.
Erma who?
Erma little teapot, short and stout!

Knock Knock!
Who's there?
Vet.
Vet who?
Vet kind of door is this without a bell?

Knock Knock!
Who's there?
Knock Knock!
Who's there?
Knock Knock!
(Repeat endlessly.)

Knock Knock!
Who's there?
Me.
Me who?
Don't you know who you are yet?

Knock Knock!
Who's there?
What.
What who?
What are you so confused about?

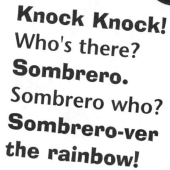

Knock Knock!
Who's there?
Huron.
Huron who?
Huron time for once!

Knock Knock!
Who's there?
Sombrero.
Sombrero who?
**Sombrero-ver
the rainbow!**

Knock Knock!
Who's there?
Desil.
Desil who?
**Desil make you
laugh if you're
not too smart!**

Knock Knock!
Who's there?
Cook.
Cook who?
**Hey! Who are you
calling cookoo?**

Knock Knock!
Who's there?
Kenzie.
Kenzie who?
Kenzie it's raining outside?

Knock Knock!
Who's there?
Carl.
Carl who?
Carl'l get you there faster than a bike!

Knock Knock!
Who's there?
Bisquick.
Bisquick who?
Bisquick, your pants are on fire!

Knock Knock!
Who's there?
Adelia.
Adelia who?
Adelia the cards, let's play snap!

Knock Knock!
Who's there?
Diploma.
Diploma who?
**Diploma will be here
in the morning!**

Knock Knock!
Who's there?
Turnip.
Turnip who?
**Turnip the music,
I love this song!**

Knock Knock!
Who's there?
Disguise.
Disguise who?
Disguise the limit!

Knock Knock!
Who's there?
Irish.
Irish who?
**Irish I had a
million pounds!**

What kind of elephants live in Antarctica?

Cold ones!

How do you fit five elephants into a car?

Two in the front, two in the back and the other in the glove compartment!

How does an elephant get out of a small car?

The same way that he got in!

Why did the elephant cross the road?

Because the chicken was having a day off!

What do you call an elephant at the North Pole?

Lost!

How does a bird with a broken wing manage to land safely?

By sparrowchute!

How do you get an elephant into a matchbox?

Take all the matches out first!

What happened to the elephant who ran away with the circus?

The police made him bring it back!

138

Knock Knock!
Who's there?
Curt.
Curt who?
Curtsie for the Queen!

Knock Knock!
Who's there?
Alexia.
Alexia who?
Alexia again to open the door!

Knock Knock!
Who's there?
Macon.
Macon who?
Have you got your Macon, it's raining!

Knock Knock!
Who's there?
Dozen.
Dozen who?
Dozen anyone live here anymore?

Knock Knock!
Who's there?
Eureka.
Eureka who?
Eureka of something, it stinks!

Knock Knock!
Who's there?
Kenya.
Kenya who?
Kenya think of anything that's more fun than geography?

Knock Knock!
Who's there?
Lorraine.
Lorraine who?
Lorraine is falling!

Knock Knock!
Who's there?
Kentucky.
Kentucky who?
Kentucky come out to play?

Knock Knock!
Who's there?
Catch.
Catch who?
Catch me if you can!

Knock Knock!
Who's there?
Eskimo.
Eskimo who?
Eskimo no questions, I'll tell you no lies!

Knock Knock!
Who's there?
Punch.
Punch who?
Not me I just got here!

Knock Knock!
Who's there?
Wire.
Wire who?
Wire you asking?

Knock Knock!
Who's there?
Waiter.
Waiter who?
**Waiter minute,
I'll tie my shoelaces!**

Knock Knock!
Who's there?
Opera.
Opera who?
**Opera-tunity. And
you thought
opportunity only
knocked once!**

Knock Knock!
Who's there?
Chimney.
Chimney who?
**Chimney cricket.
Have you seen
Pinocchio?**

Knock Knock!
Who's there?
Aileen Dover.
Aileen Dover who?
Aileen Dover and fell down!

Knock Knock!
Who's there?
Four eggs.
Four eggs who?
Four eggs ample!

Knock Knock!
Who's there?
I-8.
I-8 who?
I ate lunch already!
Is it time for dinner?

Knock Knock!
Who's there?
Walnuts.
Walnuts who?
Walnuts
around here!

Knock Knock!
Who's there?
One.
One who?
One-derful day,
isn't it?

Knock Knock!
Who's there?
Madam.
Madam who?
Madam shoe is stuck in the door!

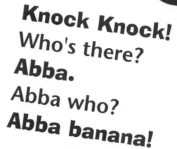

Knock Knock!
Who's there?
Abba.
Abba who?
Abba banana!

Knock Knock!
Who's there?
Disk.
Disk who?
Disk is a recorded message. Leave your answer after the beep!

Knock Knock!
Who's there?
Island.
Island who?
Island on your roof with my parachute!

Knock Knock!
Who's there?
Halle.
Halle who?
Hallelujah, you finally opened the door!

Knock Knock!
Who's there?
Tad.
Tad who?
Tad's all folks!

Knock Knock!
Who's there?
Colin.
Colin who?
Colin all doctors! Emergency!

Knock Knock!
Who's there?
Dakota.
Dakota who?
Dakota too long for the arms!

Knock Knock!
Who's there?
Heaven.
Heaven who?
Heaven you heard this joke before?

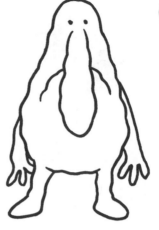

Knock Knock!
Who's there?
Roach.
Roach who?
Roach you a letter, didn't you get it?

Knock Knock!
Who's there?
Beets.
Beets who?
Beets me!

Knock Knock!
Who's there?
Queen.
Queen who?
Queen as a whistle!

Knock Knock!
Who's there?
Oswald.
Oswald who?
Oswald my gum!

Knock Knock!
Who's there?
Tex.
Tex who?
Tex two to tango!

Knock Knock!
Who's there?
Laziness.
Laziness who?
Laziness bed all day, when he should be at school!

Knock Knock!
Who's there?
Denial.
Denial who?
De Nile's a river in Egypt!

Knock Knock!
Who's there?
Rita.
Rita who?
**Rita book, you might
learn something!**

Knock Knock!
Who's there?
Says.
Says who?
Says me!

Knock Knock!
Who's there?
Haden.
Haden who?
Haden seek!

Knock Knock!
Who's there?
Sunday.
Sunday who?
**Sunday in the future,
you'll let me in!**

What kind of birds do you usually find locked up?

Jail-birds.

What is the definition of a robin?

A little bird that steals.

How many hairs are in a dog's tail?

None. They are all on the outside.

If you take your dog downtown, where should you leave him?

In a car bark.

If your dog jumped into a swimming pool, what is the first thing he would do?

Get wet.

When is the best time to buy budgies?

When they are going cheap.

What did the dog do when he broke his toe?

He called a tow truck.

What do you call a woodpecker with no beak?

A headbanger!

Knock Knock!
Who's there?
Honeycomb.
Honeycomb who?
Honeycomb your hair!

Knock Knock!
Who's there?
Don.
Don who?
Don just stand there! Say something!

Knock Knock!
Who's there?
Lulu.
Lulu who?
Lulu's not working. Can I use yours?

Knock Knock!
Who's there?
Tiss.
Tiss who?
Tiss who is good for blowing your nose!

Knock Knock!
Who's there?
Honey bee.
Honey bee who?
**Honey bee a dear
and get me a drink!**

Knock Knock!
Who's there?
Dougy.
Dougy who?
**Dougy hole in
your garden!**

Knock Knock!
Who's there?
Pierre.
Pierre who?
**Pierre through the
keyhole, you'll see!**

Knock Knock!
Who's there?
Wafer.
Wafer who?
**Wafer a long
time, but now
I'm back!**

Knock Knock!
Who's there?
Annette.
Annette who?
Annette to play tennis would be handy!

Knock Knock!
Who's there?
Ivan
Ivan who?
Ivan to suck your blood!

Knock Knock!
Who's there?
Throat.
Throat who?
Throat to me!

Knock Knock!
Who's there?
Dan.
Dan who?
Dandruff!

Knock Knock!
Who's there?
Woody.
Woody who?
**Woody you like
to know!**

Knock Knock!
Who's there?
Adolf.
Adolf who?
**Adolph ball hit me
in de mowf. Dat's
why I dawk dis way!**

Knock Knock!
Who's there?
Jess.
Jess who?
Jess me and my shadow!

Knock Knock!
Who's there?
Harmony.
Harmony who?
**Harmony knock
knock jokes do you
expect me to know?**

Knock Knock!
Who's there?
Amsterdam.
Amsterdam who?
Amsterdam tired of all these stupid knock knock jokes!

Knock Knock!
Who's there?
Tennessee.
Tennessee who?
Tennessee you tonight!

Knock Knock!
Who's there?
Hugo.
Hugo who?
Hugo jump in the lake!

Knock Knock!
Who's there?
Quiet Tina.
Quiet Tina who?
Quiet Tina classroom!

Knock Knock!
Who's there?
Penguin.
Penguin who?
Penguin swimming!

Knock Knock!
Who's there?
Whoopi.
Whoopi who?
Whoopi cushion!

Knock Knock!
Who's there?
Tunis.
Tunis who?
**Tunis company,
three's a crowd!**

Knock Knock!
Who's there?
Owl.
Owl who?
Owl be back later!

Knock Knock!
Who's there?
Helium.
Helium who?
Helium, ah, um, ah, have to go!

Knock Knock!
Who's there?
Who.
Who who?
Who Who Hip who ray!

Knock Knock!
Who's there?
Cindy.
Cindy who?
Cindy firetruck fast!

Knock Knock!
Who's there?
Ada.
Ada who?
Ada enough now!

Knock Knock!
Who's there?
Acid.
Acid who?
**Acid down and
be quiet!**

Knock Knock!
Who's there?
Tiffany!
Tiffany who?
**Tiffany rubbish out
the bin, will you?**

Knock Knock!
Who's there?
Tibet!
Tibet who?
**Early Tibet and
early to rise!**

Knock Knock!
Who's there?
Hammond.
Hammond who?
Hammond eggs!

Why did the fly fly?
Because the spider spied 'er!

Why did the firefly keep stealing things?

He was light fingered!

What goes 'snap, crackle and pop'?

A firefly with a short circuit!

Which fly makes films?

Steven Spielbug!

Why were the flies playing football in a saucer?

They were playing for the cup!

How do fireflies start a race?

Ready, steady, glow!

If there are five flies in the kitchen how do you know which one is the American Football player?

It's the one in the sugar bowl!

What did one firefly say to the other?

"Got to glow now!"

What is green, sooty and whistles when it rubs its back legs together?

Chimney Cricket!

What is a grasshopper?

An insect on a pogo stick!

Where do freshwater fish keep their savings?

In a river bank.

What's worse than a camel with backache?

A millipede with athlete's foot!

Which bird can lift the heaviest weight?

A crane.

What is the best year for kangaroos?

A leap year.

What do you call a bear without an ear?

B!

What is green and can jump a mile in a minute?

A grasshopper with hiccups!

Knock Knock!
Who's there?
Dawn.
Dawn who?
Dawn do anything I wouldn't do!

Knock Knock!
Who's there?
Sarah.
Sarah who?
Sarah grown-up in the house?

Knock Knock!
Who's there?
Wilfred.
Wilfred who?
Wilfred like his present?

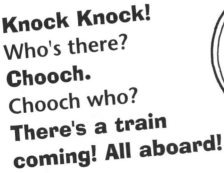

Knock Knock!
Who's there?
Chooch.
Chooch who?
There's a train coming! All aboard!

Knock Knock!
Who's there?
Wendy.
Wendy who?
**Wendy clock
strikes twelve,
I'll turn back into
a pumpkin!**

Knock Knock!
Who's there?
Elaine.
Elaine who?
**Elaine of traffic is
backed up for miles!**

Knock Knock!
Who's there?
Lemmy.
Lemmy who?
Lemme go!

Knock Knock!
Who's there?
Sally.
Sally who?
**Sally-brate good
times, come on!
It's a Sally-bration!**

What kind of dog chases anything red?

A bull dog!

What kind of dog wears a uniform and medals?

A guard dog!

What do you call a dog in jeans and a sweater?

A plain clothes police dog!

What do you get if you cross a sheepdog with a jelly?

The collie wobbles!

What do you call a dog in the middle of a muddy road?

A mutt in a rut!

When is a black dog not a black dog?

When it's a greyhound!

What goes 'zzub, zzub'?

A bee flying backwards!

How does a lion greet you ?

"Pleased to eat you!"

What do you call a bee born in May?

A maybe!

What kind of bee can't be understood?

A mumble bee!

What do you get if you cross a dog with a blind mole?

A dog that keeps barking up the wrong tree!

What do you get if you cross a gun dog with a telephone?

A golden receiver!

What do you get if you cross a Beatle and an Australian dog?

Dingo Starr!

What happens to a dog that keeps eating bits off the table?

He gets splinters in his mouth!

What do you get if you cross a dog and a skunk?

Rid of the dog!

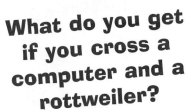

What do you get if you cross a computer and a rottweiler?

A computer with a lot of bites!

What do you get if you cross a dog with a kangaroo?

A dog that has somewhere to put its own lead!

What do you get if you cross a dog and a sheep?

A sheep that can round itself up!

What do you get if you cross a dog and a lion?

A terrified postman!

What do you get if you cross two young dogs with a pair of headphones?

Hush puppies!

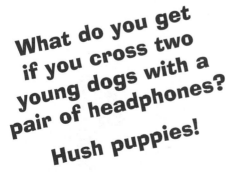

What do you get if you cross a dog with a frog?

A dog that can lick you from the other side of the road!

What do you call a litter of young dogs who have come in from the snow?

Slush puppies!

What do you call a dog with no legs?

It doesn't matter what you call him, he still won't come!

What makes a glow-worm glow?

A light meal!

What kind of doctors are like spiders?

Spin doctors!

What is the difference between a flea-bitten dog and a bored visitor?

One's going to itch and the other is itching to go!

Why are spiders like tops?

They are always spinning!

What has eight legs and likes living in trees?

Four orangutans.

What did
the wife spider say
to her husband when
he tried to explain
why he was late?

"You're spinning me
a yarn here!"

What is the
difference between
school dinners and a
pile of slugs?

School dinners come
on a plate!

What did the slug
say as he slipped
down the wall?

"How slime flies!"

How do you know your
kitchen floor is dirty?

The slugs leave
a trail on the floor
that reads 'clean me!'

Why did the sparrow go to the library?

It was looking for bookworms!

What is life like for a woodworm?

Boring!

How do you feel if you cross a sheepdog with a melon?

Melon-collie!

What do you call a black Eskimo dog?

A dusky husky!

What do you get if you cross a cocker spaniel, a poodle and a rooster?

Cockerpoodledoo!

What do you call a sheepdog's tail that can tell tall stories?

A shaggy dog's tale!

Why did the dog have a gleam in his eye?

Someone bumped his elbow while he was brushing his teeth.

Why do dogs run in circles?

Because it's hard to run in squares!

How did the little Scottish dog feel when he saw a monster?

Terrier-fied!

How do you find your dog if he's lost in the woods?

Put your ear up to a tree and listen for the bark!

Eleven dogs shared one umbrella, yet none got wet. How?

It wasn't raining.

How can you tell a dog from a jar of peanut butter?

The dog doesn't stick to the roof of your mouth.

How can you tell a dog from a tomato?

The tomato is red.

How can you tell a dog from an elephant?

The elephant remembers.

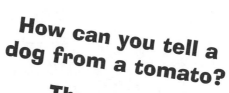

What happened when the lion ate the comedian?

He felt funny.

How did the dog make anti-freeze?

He stole her blanket.

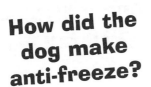

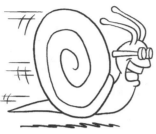

Knock Knock!
Who's there?
Wheelbarrow.
Wheelbarrow who?
Wheelbarrow some money and go on holiday!

Knock Knock!
Who's there?
Benny.
Benny who?
Benny long time since I saw you!

Knock Knock!
Who's there?
Lena.
Lena who?
Lena a little closer and I'll tell you!

Knock Knock!
Who's there?
Zippy.
Zippy who?
Zippy dee-doo-dah, zippy dee hey!

Knock Knock!
Who's there?
Lee King.
Lee King who?
Lee King bucket!

Knock Knock!
Who's there?
Tennis.
Tennis who?
Tennis five plus five!

Knock Knock!
Who's there?
Eames.
Eames who?
Eames to please!

Knock Knock!
Who's there?
Utica.
Utica who?
Utica the high road and I'll take the low road!

Knock Knock!
Who's there?
Fanny.
Fanny who?
Fanny body calls, I'm out!

Knock Knock!
Who's there?
Hand.
Hand who?
Hand over your wallet, this is a stick up!

Knock Knock!
Who's there?
Thayer.
Thayer who?
Thayer thorry and I won't throw this pie in your face!

Knock Knock!
Who's there?
Barry.
Barry who?
Barry the treasure where no one will find it!

Knock Knock!
Who's there?
Urchin.
Urchin who?
Urchin is pointy!

Knock Knock!
Who's there?
Beezer.
Beezer who?
Beezer black and yellow and make honey!

Knock Knock!
Who's there?
Weirdo.
Weirdo who?
Weirdo you think you're going?

Knock Knock!
Who's there?
UCI.
UCI who?
UCI had to ring because you didn't answer when I knocked!

Knock Knock!
Who's there?
Falafel.
Falafel who?
Falafel off his bike and hurt his knee!

Knock Knock!
Who's there?
John.
John who?
John the Navy!

Knock Knock!
Who's there?
Daisy.
Daisy who?
Daisy that you are in, but I don't believe them!

Knock Knock!
Who's there?
UB40
UB40 who?
UB40 today. Happy birthday!

Knock Knock!
Who's there?
Gerald.
Gerald who?
Gerald washed up!

Knock Knock!
Who's there?
Sam.
Sam who?
Sam person who knocked on the door last time!

Knock Knock!
Who's there?
Lucretia.
Lucretia who?
Lucretia from the Black Lagoon!

Knock Knock!
Who's there?
Titus.
Titus who?
Titus it can be!

Knock Knock!
Who's there?
Valencia.
Valencia who?
Valencia pound. When will I get it back?

Knock Knock!
Who's there?
Foster.
Foster who?
Foster than a speeding bullet!

Knock Knock!
Who's there?
Les.
Les who?
Les go for a swim!

Knock Knock!
Who's there?
Garden.
Garden who?
**Garden the
treasure!**

Knock Knock!
Who's there?
Sherlock.
Sherlock who?
**Sherlock your door!
Someone could
break in ...**

Knock Knock!
Who's there?
Actor.
Actor who?
Actor you, my dear!

Knock Knock!
Who's there?
Sadie.
Sadie who?
Sadie Pledge of Allegiance!

Knock Knock!
Who's there?
Jacklyn.
Jacklyn who?
Jacklyn Hyde!

Knock Knock!
Who's there?
Major.
Major who?
Major headache, please gimme aspirin!

Knock Knock!
Who's there?
Gary.
Gary who?
Gary on smiling!

Knock Knock!
Who's there?
K-2.
K-2 who?
K-2 come in!

Knock Knock!
Who's there?
Knock knock!
Who's there?
Knock Knock!
Who's there?
I'm sorry, but my mother doesn't allow me to speak to strangers!

Knock Knock!
Who's there?
Hacienda.
Hacienda who?
Hacienda the story!

Knock Knock!
Who's there?
Manny.
Manny who?
Manny people keep asking me that!

Knock Knock!
Who's there?
Zombie.
Zombie who?
Zombies make honey, others are queens!

Knock Knock!
Who's there?
Knee.
Knee who?
Knee-d you ask?

Knock Knock!
Who's there?
Pasta.
Pasta who?
Pasta salt, please!

Knock Knock!
Who's there?
Raoul.
Raoul who?
Raoul with the punches!

Knock Knock!
Who's there?
Russian.
Russian who?
Russian about makes me tired!

Knock Knock!
Who's there?
Meg.
Meg who?
Meg me a drink!

Knock Knock!
Who's there?
Japan.
Japan who?
Japan is too hot, ouch!

Knock Knock!
Who's there?
Yacht.
Yacht who?
**Yacht a know
me by now!**

Knock Knock!
Who's there?
Nine.
Nine who?
Nine danke!

Knock Knock!
Who's there?
Phoebe.
Phoebe who?
**Phoebe too high
for us to pay!**

Knock Knock!
Who's there?
Miss Piggy.
Miss Piggy who?
**Miss Piggy went to
market, Miss Piggy
stayed at home ...**

Knock Knock!
Who's there?
Juno.
Juno who?
I dunno, Juno?

Knock Knock!
Who's there?
Moira.
Moira who?
The Moira the merrier!

Knock Knock!
Who's there?
Xena.
Xena who?
Xena minute!

Knock Knock!
Who's there?
Germaine.
Germaine who?
Germaine you don't recognise me?

Knock Knock!
Who's there?
Sharon!
Sharon who?
Sharon share alike!

Knock Knock!
Who's there?
Percy.
Percy who?
Percy-vere and you'll succeed!

Knock Knock!
Who's there?
Iraq.
Iraq who?
Iraq of lamb!

Knock Knock!
Who's there?
Dwayne.
Dwayne who?
Dwayne the bath tub, I'm drowning!

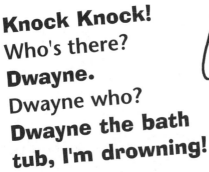

Knock Knock!
Who's there?
Mistake.
Mistake who?
**Mistake medicine
if you are poorly!**

Knock Knock!
Who's there?
Shower.
Shower who?
**Shower you care,
send her some
chocolates!**

Knock Knock!
Who's there?
Germany.
Germany who?
**Germany people
knocking on
your door?**

Knock Knock!
Who's there?
Oui.
Oui who?
**Oui will, oui
will, rock you!**

How did the dog make gold soup?

He put in 24 carrots.

How did the dog's owner know his pet was angry about having soap flakes for breakfast?

He foamed at the mouth.

How do you keep a dog from barking in your front garden?

Put him in your back garden.

How do you make a dog float?

Take two scoops of ice cream, some fizzy drink and a small dog.

**How is a
cowardly dog
like a
leaky tap?**

They both run.

How is a dog like a penny?

**They both have a
head and a tail.**

**What do you
call a very
rude bird?**

A mockingbird.

**Which birds steal
soap from baths?**

Robber ducks!

Why did the moth nibble a hole in the carpet?

He wanted to see the floor show!

What's the biggest moth in the world?

A mammoth!

Why was the moth so unpopular?

He kept picking holes in everything!

What did the spider say when he broke his new web?

Darn it!

What is a myth?
A female moth!

What happened when the chef found a daddy long legs in the salad?

It became a daddy short legs!

What do you get if you cross a tarantula with a rose?

I'm not sure, but I wouldn't try smelling it.

Why did the spider buy a car?

So he could take it out for a spin!

Knock Knock!
Who's there?
Iris.
Iris who?
Iris Tew in the name of the law!

Knock Knock!
Who's there?
Unite.
Unite who?
Unite a person, you call him Sir!

Knock Knock!
Who's there?
Goblin.
Goblin who?
Goblin your candy will make your tummy ache!

Knock Knock!
Who's there?
Hannah.
Hannah who?
Hannah Happy New Year!

Knock Knock!
Who's there?
Barbara.
Barbara who?
**Barbara, black sheep,
have you any wool?**

Knock Knock!
Who's there?
Cereal.
Cereal who?
**Cereal pleasure
to meet you!**

Knock Knock!
Who's there?
Hiram.
Hiram who?
**Hiram fine, how
are you?**

Knock Knock!
Who's there?
Felix.
Felix who?
Felix-cited all over!

Where would you put an injured insect?

In an antbulance!

What do you get if you cross the Lone Ranger with an insect?

The masked-quito!

What has antlers and sucks blood?

A moose-quito!

Why did the mosquito go to the dentist?

To improve his bite!

What is a mosquito's favourite sport?

Skin-diving!

How do you know if you have a tough mosquito?

You slap him and he slaps you back!

What is the difference between a mosquito and a fly?

Try sewing buttons on a mosquito!

What's the difference between a zombie and a mosquito?

A mosquito drops off you when you die!

Knock Knock!
Who's there?
Ask me.
Ask me who?
Ask me inside and you'll find out!

Knock Knock!
Who's there?
Mustard.
Mustard who?
Mustard left it in the car!

Knock Knock!
Who's there?
Ireland.
Ireland who?
Ireland you some money if you promise to pay me back!

Knock Knock!
Who's there?
Rapunzel.
Rapunzel who?
Rapunzel troubles in your old kitbag and smile, smile, smile!

Knock Knock!
Who's there?
Poker.
Poker who?
**Poker and see
if she's awake!**

Knock Knock!
Who's there?
Isaac.
Isaac who?
**Isaac'ly who do
you think this is?**

Knock Knock!
Who's there?
Ivory.
Ivory who?
**Ivory strong
like Tarzan!**

Knock Knock!
Who's there?
Owl.
Owl who?
**Owl I can say is
'Knock, knock!'**

What's a glow-worm's favourite song?

Wake me up before you glow-glow!

Why was the glow-worm unhappy?

Because her children weren't that bright!

What do you get if you cross a glow-worm with some beer?

Light ale!

What do you get if you cross a worm and a young goat?

A dirty kid!

What do worms leave around their baths?

The scum of the earth!

What did one maggot say to another?

"What's a nice maggot like you doing in a joint like this!"

What did the woodworm say to the chair?

"It's been nice gnawing you!"

What's yellow, wriggles and is dangerous?

A maggot with attitude!

Knock Knock!
Who's there?
Urinal.
Urinal who?
Urinal lot of trouble!

Knock Knock!
Who's there?
Pepperoni.
Pepperoni who?
Pepperoni makes me sneeze!

Knock Knock!
Who's there?
Izzy.
Izzy who?
Izzy come, Izzy go!

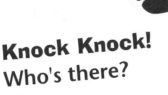

Knock Knock!
Who's there?
Me.
Me who?
Meeow!

Knock Knock!
Who's there?
Salmon.
Salmon who?
Salmon enchanted evening!

Knock Knock!
Who's there?
Pickle.
Pickle who?
Pickle little flower and give it to your mother!

Knock Knock!
Who's there?
Hodedofo.
Hodedofo who?
Hodedofo me, my arms are full!

How do you catch a
runaway dog?

Hide behind a tree
and make a noise
like a bone!

What dog loves to
take bubble baths?

A shampoodle!

What kind of dog
does a vampire
prefer?

Any kind of
bloodhound!

What dogs are best
for sending
telegrams?

Wire-haired terriers.

What is a dog's favourite city?

New Yorkie!

Who is a dog's favourite comedian?

Growlcho Marx!

What did the cowboy say when the bear ate Lassie?

"Well, doggone!"

What do you get if you take a really big dog out for a walk?

A great dane out!

Knock Knock!
Who's there?
Paul.
Paul who?
Paul a fast one!

Knock Knock!
Who's there?
Armageddon.
Armageddon who?
Armageddon out of here!

Knock Knock!
Who's there?
Courtney.
Courtney who?
Courtney burglars recently!

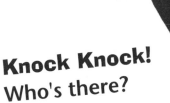

Knock Knock!
Who's there?
Genoa.
Genoa who?
Genoa any new knock knock jokes?

Knock Knock!
Who's there?
Steve.
Steve who?
Steve upper lip!

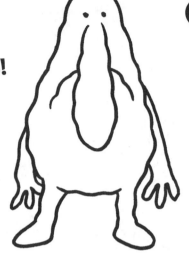

Knock Knock!
Who's there?
Douglas.
Douglas who?
Douglas is broken!

Knock Knock!
Who's there?
Luke.
Luke who?
Luke before you leap!

Knock Knock!
Who's there?
Noah.
Noah who?
Noah body knows the trouble I go through!

Knock Knock!
Who's there?
Paula.
Paula who?
Paula up the door handle, will you, and let me in!

Knock Knock!
Who's there?
Gerald.
Gerald who?
Gerald friend (insert name)!

Knock Knock!
Who's there?
Bingo.
Bingo who?
Bingo'ing to come and see you for ages!

Knock Knock!
Who's there?
Jenny.
Jenny who?
Jenny'd some help opening the door, it's taking you long enough!

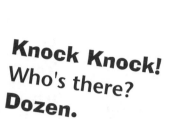

Knock Knock!
Who's there?
Horace.
Horace who?
Horace-scopes can be fun!

Knock Knock!
Who's there?
Dozen.
Dozen who?
Dozen anybody want to play with me?

Knock Knock!
Who's there?
Heart.
Heart who?
Heart to hear you, speak up a bit!

Knock Knock!
Who's there?
Amnesia.
Amnesia who?
Oh, I see you have it too!

Knock Knock!
Who's there?
Armada.
Armada who?
Armada told us there'd be days like this.

Knock Knock!
Who's there?
Dwight.
Dwight who?
Dwight stuff on your mouth!

Knock Knock!
Who's there?
Mary Queen of Scots.
Mary Queen of Scots who?
Mary Queen of Scots who? Didn't you learn anything in history class?

Knock Knock!
Who's there?
Whij.
Whij who?
Whij one of you locked the door?

Knock Knock!
Who's there?
Turnip.
Turnip who?
Turnip the radio, please!

Knock Knock!
Who's there?
Trees are.
Trees are who?
Trees are green!

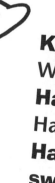

Knock Knock!
Who's there?
Abbey.
Abbey who?
Abbey birthday to you!

Knock Knock!
Who's there?
Halibut.
Halibut who?
Halibut a kiss, sweetie?

Knock Knock!
Who's there?
Earl.
Earl who?
Earl be glad to get to bed, I'm tired!

Knock Knock!
Who's there?
Yukon.
Yukon who?
Yukon say that again!

Knock Knock!
Who's there?
Bab.
Bab who?
Bab-boone is a real ape!

Knock Knock!
Who's there?
Earwig.
Earwig who?
Earwigo, earwigo, earwigo!

Knock Knock!
Who's there?
Texas.
Texas who?
Texas are getting higher every year!

Knock Knock!
Who's there?
Bed.
Bed who?
Bed you can't guess I've got a cold!

Knock Knock!
Who's there?
Toronto.
Toronto who?
Toronto be a law against these knock knock jokes!

Knock Knock!
Who's there?
Walnuts.
Walnuts who?
Walnuts around here!

Knock Knock!
Who's there?
Hammond.
Hammond who?
Hammond cheese on toast, please!

Knock Knock!
Who's there?
Crispin.
Crispin who?
Crispin crunchy is how I like my apples!

Knock Knock!
Who's there?
Odysseus.
Odysseus who?
Odysseus the last straw!

Knock Knock!
Who's there?
Ridya.
Ridya who?
Ridya bike and you'll get there quicker!

Knock Knock!
Who's there?
Wizard.
Wizard who?
Wizard you I'm lost!

Knock Knock!
Who's there?
Earlier.
Earlier who?
Earlier fly is undone!

Knock Knock!
Who's there?
Anderson.
Anderson who?
Anderson and daughter came too!

Knock Knock!
Who's there?
Bean.
Bean who?
Bean working very hard today!

Knock Knock!
Who's there?
Watusi.
Watusi who?
Watusi is what you get!

Knock Knock!
Who's there?
Edith.
Edith who?
Edith, it'll make you feel better!

Knock Knock!
Who's there?
Thumb.
Thumb who?
Thumb like it hot, some like it cold!

Knock Knock!
Who's there?
Carol.
Carol who?
**Carol go if you turn
the ignition key!**

Knock Knock!
Who's there?
Tyrone.
Tyrone who?
Tyrone shoelaces!

Knock Knock!
Who's there?
Danielle.
Danielle who?
**Danielle at me,
it's not my fault!**

Knock Knock!
Who's there?
Hans.
Hans who?
Hans off the table!

Knock Knock!
Who's there?
Michelle.
Michelle who?
Michelle sea shells on the sea shore!

Knock Knock!
Who's there?
Billy.
Billy who?
Billy goat gruff!

Knock Knock!
Who's there?
Marmite.
Marmite who?
Marmite but Pa won't!

Knock Knock!
Who's there?
Bertha.
Bertha who?
Bertha day greetings!

Knock Knock!
Who's there?
Tuba.
Tuba who?
Tuba toothpaste!

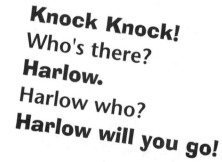

Knock Knock!
Who's there?
Harlow.
Harlow who?
Harlow will you go!

Knock Knock!
Who's there?
Hugo.
Hugo who?
Hugo to bed now!

Knock Knock!
Who's there?
Dana.
Dana who?
**Dana talk with
your mouth full!**

Knock Knock!
Who's there?
Patty O.
Patty O who?
**Patty O
furniture!**

Knock Knock!
Who's there?
Sweden.
Sweden who?
**Sweden sour is
my favourite
Chinese meal!**

Knock Knock!
Who's there?
Boxer.
Boxer who?
Boxer tricks!

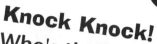

Knock Knock!
Who's there?
Goose.
Goose who?
Goose who's knocking!

Knock Knock!
Who's there?
Sari.
Sari who?
Sari I was sarong!

Knock Knock!
Who's there?
Dai.
Dai who?
Dai Larfin.

Knock Knock!
Who's there?
Stew.
Stew who?
Stew early to go to bed!

Knock Knock!
Who's there?
Emma.
Emma who?
Emma glad you asked me that!

Knock Knock!
Who's there?
Carrie.
Carrie who?
Carrie me home, I'm tired!

Knock Knock!
Who's there?
Harold.
Harold who?
Harold are you?

Knock Knock!
Who's there?
Abel.
Abel who.
Abel seaman!

Knock Knock!
Who's there?
Wanda.
Wanda who?
Wanda have another drink?

Knock Knock!
Who's there?
Ellis.
Ellis who?
Ellis before 'M'!

Knock Knock!
Who's there?
Kaye.
Kaye who?
Kaye sera sera!

Knock Knock!
Who's there?
Puss.
Puss who?
Puss your bike, it's safer!

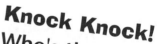

Knock Knock!
Who's there?
Hijack.
Hijack who?
Hijack, how's Jill?

Knock Knock!
Who's there?
Elsie.
Elsie who?
Elsie you around!

Knock Knock!
Who's there?
Laurie.
Laurie who?
Laurie driver!

Knock Knock!
Who's there?
Fozzie.
Fozzie who?
Fozzie hundreth time, my name is Ben!

Knock Knock!
Who's there?
Mica.
Mica who?
Mica is double parked!

Knock Knock!
Who's there?
Philippa.
Philippa who?
**Philippa bath tub,
I'm dirty!**

Knock Knock!
Who's there?
Heidi.
Heidi who?
**Heidi-clare war
on you!**

Knock Knock!
Who's there?
Ewan.
Ewan who?
No, just me!

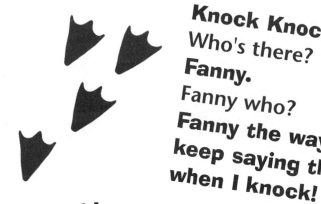

Knock Knock!
Who's there?
Fanny.
Fanny who?
Fanny the way you keep saying that when I knock!

Knock Knock!
Who's there?
Butcher.
Butcher who?
Butcher left leg in, your left leg out!

Knock Knock!
Who's there?
Alan.
Alan who?
Alan't my lesson!

Knock Knock!
Who's there?
Hey.
Hey who?
Hey ho, hey ho, it's off to work we go!

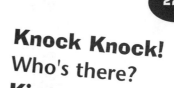

Knock Knock!
Who's there?
Lady.
Lady who?
Lady law down!

Knock Knock!
Who's there?
Kipper.
Kipper who?
**Kipper hands
to yourself!**

Knock Knock!
Who's there?
Bug.
Bug who?
Bug-sy Malone!

Knock Knock!
Who's there?
Boo.
Boo who?
**Just boo.
I'm a ghost!**

Knock Knock!
Who's there?
Fitzwilliam.
Fitzwilliam who?
Fitzwilliam better than it fits me!

Knock Knock!
Who's there?
Custer.
Custer who?
Custer penny to find out!

Knock Knock!
Who's there?
Michelle.
Michelle who?
Michelle had a big crab inside it!

Knock Knock!
Who's there?
Lucinda.
Lucinda who?
Lucinda chain, I want to get in!

Knock Knock!
Who's there?
Tobias.
Tobias who?
**Tobias a pig,
that's why I
went to market!**

Knock Knock!
Who's there?
Janet.
Janet who?
**Janet has too many
holes in it, the fish
will escape!**

Knock Knock!
Who's there?
Paul.
Paul who?
**Paul hard, the door's
stuck again!**

Knock Knock!
Who's there?
Midas.
Midas who?
Midas well open the door!

Knock Knock!
Who's there?
Bruce.
Bruce who?
I bruce easily, be gentle!

Knock Knock!
Who's there?
Honeydew.
Honeydew who?
Honeydew you want to come out tonight?

Knock Knock!
Who's there?
Arthur.
Arthur who?
Arthur-mometer is good for measuring temperature!

Knock Knock!
Who's there?
Deena.
Deena who?
Deena you hear the first time?

Knock Knock!
Who's there?
Harold.
Harold who?
Harold do you think I look?

Knock Knock!
Who's there?
Sonia.
Sonia who?
Sonia paper boy making a delivery!

Knock Knock!
Who's there?
Colin.
Colin who?
Colin and see me on the way home!

Knock Knock!
Who's there?
Matt.
Matt who?
Mattadore!

Knock Knock!
Who's there?
Rocky.
Rocky who?
Rocky bye baby on the tree top!

Knock Knock!
Who's there?
Olaf.
Olaf who?
Olaf if you think it's funny!

Knock Knock!
Who's there?
Enoch.
Enoch who?
Enoch and enoch, but nobody opens the door!

Knock Knock!
Who's there?
Dinaminute.
Dinaminute who?
Dinaminute if you ask her nicely!

Knock Knock!
Who's there?
Amy.
Amy who?
**Amy'fraid
I've forgotten!**

Knock Knock!
Who's there?
Roxanne.
Roxanne who?
**Roxanne pebbles are
all over the beach!**

Knock Knock!
Who's there?
Iris.
Iris who?
Iris you were here!

Knock Knock!
Who's there?
Tilly.
Tilly who?
Are you going on a fox hunt?

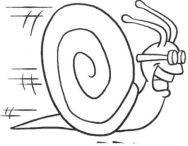

Knock Knock!
Who's there?
York.
York who?
York coming over to our place!

Knock Knock!
Who's there?
Meg.
Meg who?
Meg your bed before breakfast!

Knock Knock!
Who's there?
Heywood, Hugh and Harry.
Heywood Hugh and Harry who?
Heywood Hugh Harry up and open the door!

Knock Knock!
Who's there?
Lena.
Lena who?
Lena little closer and I'll tell you!

Knock Knock!
Who's there?
Rhoda.
Rhoda who?
I rhoda camel to school and my teacher got the hump!

Knock Knock!
Who's there?
Mister.
Mister who?
I mister last bus home!

Knock Knock!
Who's there?
Diana.
Diana who?
Diana thirst, can I have some water please?

Knock Knock!
Who's there?
Eugenie.
Eugenie who?
Eugenie from the bottle, I'll give you three wishes!

Knock Knock!
Who's there?
Alice.
Alice who?
**Alice N. Tew if
you listen to me!**

Knock Knock!
Who's there?
Matthew.
Matthew who?
**Matthew lace has
come undone!**

Knock Knock!
Who's there?
Daryl.
Daryl who?
**Daryl never be
another you!**

Knock Knock!
Who's there?
Max.
Max who?
**Max no difference
to you, just let
me in!**

Knock Knock!
Who's there?
Bridget.
Bridget who?
London Bridget falling down, falling down.

Knock Knock!
Who's there?
Oscar.
Oscar who?
Oscar if she wants a drink!

Knock Knock!
Who's there?
Althea.
Althea who?
Althea later in the afternoon!

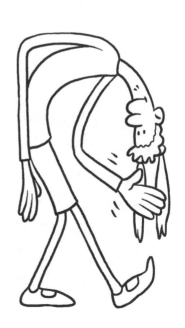

Knock Knock!
Who's there?
Toodle.
Toodle who?
Bye bye!

Knock Knock!
Who's there?
Europe.
Europe who?
Europe early this morning!

Knock Knock!
Who's there?
Norman.
Norman who?
Norman has ever set foot in here before!

Knock Knock!
Who's there?
Farmer.
Farmer who?
Farmer people here than there were last year!

Knock Knock!
Who's there?
Musket.
Musket who?
Musket in, it's urgent!

Knock Knock!
Who's there?
Tuna.
Tuna who?
**Tuna radio down,
I'm trying to sleep!**

Knock Knock!
Who's there?
Hobbit.
Hobbit who?
**Hobbit letting
me in then!**

Knock Knock!
Who's there?
Amanda.
Amanda who?
Amanda-rin!

Knock Knock!
Who's there?
Fido.
Fido who?
**Fido I have to
wait here!**

Knock Knock!
Who's there?
Eliza.
Eliza who?
**Eliza wake at night
thinking about this door!**

Knock Knock!
Who's there?
One-eye.
One-eye who?
**You're the one-eye
care for!**

Knock Knock!
Who's there?
Pill.
Pill who?
**Yes please, and a
sheet to go with it!**

Knock Knock!
Who's there?
Pencil.
Pencil who?
**Your pencil fall down
if the elastic goes!**

Knock Knock!
Who's there?
Gutter.
Gutter who?
Gutter get in, it's freezing out here!

Knock Knock!
Who's there?
Owen.
Owen who?
Owen are you going to let me in?

Knock Knock!
Who's there?
Howell.
Howell who?
Howell you have your toast, marmalade or jam?

Knock Knock!
Who's there?
Hayden.
Hayden who?
Hayden seek is fun to play!

Knock Knock!
Who's there?
Ollie.
Ollie who?
Ollie time you do that I want to scream!

Knock Knock!
Who's there?
Denver.
Denver who?
Denver the good old days!

Knock Knock!
Who's there?
Hurd.
Hurd who?
Hurd my hand so I can't knock!

Knock Knock!
Who's there?
Odessa.
Odessa who?
Odessa really fun joke!

Knock Knock!
Who's there?
Tuna.
Tuna who?
Tuna violin and it will sound better!

Knock Knock!
Who's there?
Cynthia.
Cynthia who?
Cynthia been gone I miss you very much!

Knock Knock!
Who's there?
Murray.
Murray who?
Murray me! Not likely ...

Knock Knock!
Who's there?
Gus.
Gus who?
That's what you're supposed to do!

246

Why shouldn't you take an elephant to the zoo?

Because he'd rather go to the movies!

Where do little fish go every morning?

To plaice school!

Where do fish wash?

In a river basin!

What do you say to a mouse that's chipped its front tooth?

"Hard cheese."

Why did the zebra cross the road?

To make a zebra crossing.

What is green and pecks on trees?

Woody Wood Pickle.

What do you call a bunch of chickens playing hide-and-seek?

Fowl play.

What's got six legs and can fly long distance?

Three swallows.

Knock Knock!
Who's there?
Scissor.
Scissor who?
Scissor or Cleopatra!

Knock Knock!
Who's there?
Roland.
Roland who?
Roland stone gathers no moss!

Knock Knock!
Who's there?
Cannelloni.
Cannelloni who?
Cannelloni some money until next week?

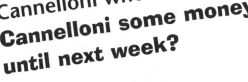

Knock Knock!
Who's there?
Plato.
Plato who?
Plato fish and chips please!

Knock Knock!
Who's there?
Sofa.
Sofa who?
Sofa so good!

Knock Knock!
Who's there?
Cindy.
Cindy who?
**Cindy next one
in please!**

Knock Knock!
Who's there?
Indonesia.
Indonesia who?
**I get weak Indonesia
when I look at you!**

Knock Knock!
Who's there?
Luke.
Luke who?
**Luke before
you leap!**

Knock Knock!
Who's there?
Weevil.
Weevil who?
Weevil only be staying a minute!

Knock Knock!
Who's there?
Pasture.
Pasture who?
Pasture bed time, isn't it?

Knock Knock!
Who's there?
Ella.
Ella who?
Ella-vator. Doesn't that give you a lift!

Knock Knock!
Who's there?
Otis.
Otis who?
Otis a wonderful day to walk in the park!

Knock Knock!
Who's there?
Marmalade.
Marmalade who?
Marmalade me an egg for breakfast!

Knock Knock!
Who's there?
Dotty.
Dotty who?
Dotty way the cookie crumbles!

Knock Knock!
Who's there?
Spook.
Spook who?
Spook-etti!

Knock Knock!
Who's there?
Yulla.
Yulla who?
Yulla catch more flies with honey and vinegar!

Knock Knock!
Who's there?
Holmes.
Holmes who?
Holmes where the heart is!

Knock Knock!
Who's there?
Ellie.
Ellie who?
Ellie-phants never forget!

Knock Knock!
Who's there?
Atlas.
Atlas who?
Atlas it's Friday, the weekend's nearly here!

Knock Knock!
Who's there?
Summertime.
Summertime who?
Summertime you're a pest!

Knock Knock!
Who's there?
Juicy.
Juicy who?
Juicy the sign on the door?

Knock Knock!
Who's there?
Atomic.
Atomic who?
Atomic ache!

Knock Knock!
Who's there?
Catskill.
Catskill who?
Catskill mice!

Knock Knock!
Who's there?
Illegals.
Illegals who?
Illegals stay in the nest until they feel better!

Knock Knock!
Who's there?
Seymour.
Seymour who?
Seymour if you look out the window!

Knock Knock!
Who's there?
Darius.
Darius who?
Darius a lot of things I have to tell you!

Knock Knock!
Who's there?
Francis.
Francis who?
Francis where people speak French!

Knock Knock!
Who's there?
Saul.
Saul who?
Saul the king's horses and saul the king's men!

Knock Knock!
Who's there?
Omega.
Omega who?
Omega the best man win!

Knock Knock!
Who's there?
Carlotta.
Carlotta who?
Carlotta trouble when it breaks down!

Knock Knock!
Who's there?
Heifer.
Heifer who?
Heifer sixpence is better than half a penny!

Knock Knock!
Who's there?
Emile.
Emile who?
Emile fit for a king!

Knock Knock!
Who's there?
Alfalfa.
Alfalfa who?
Alfalfa you if you fall for me!

Knock Knock!
Who's there?
Yukon.
Yukon who?
Yukon fool some people all the time!

Knock Knock!
Who's there?
Walrus.
Walrus who?
Why do you walrus ask the same question?

Knock Knock!
Who's there?
Gopher.
Gopher who?
Gopher it and you might win!

Knock Knock!
Who's there?
Romeo.
Romeo who?
Romeo ver to the other side of the lake!

Knock Knock!
Who's there?
Oslo.
Oslo who?
Oslo down, what's the hurry?

Knock Knock!
Who's there?
Typhoid.
Typhoid who?
Typhoid that song before!

Knock Knock!
Who's there?
Fodder.
Fodder who?
Fodder and mother are taking me for a picnic!

Knock Knock!
Who's there?
Cattle.
Cattle who?
Cattle always purr when you stroke it!

Knock Knock!
Who's there?
Spook.
Spook who?
Spook only when you are spoken to!

Knock Knock!
Who's there?
Aida.
Aida who?
Aida lot of green apples, now I feel sick!

Knock Knock!
Who's there?
Celeste.
Celeste who?
Celeste time I'm telling you! Open up!

Knock Knock!
Who's there?
Anatole.
Anatole who?
Anatole me you're so annoying!

Knock Knock!
Who's there?
Frank Lee.
Frank Lee who?
Frank Lee I don't care!

Knock Knock!
Who's there?
Acid.
Acid who?
Acid-down and be quiet!

Knock Knock!
Who's there?
Chin up.
Chin up who?
Chin up, I'm not going to tell anymore knock knock jokes!

Why did the
owl,'owl?

Because the
woodpecker would
peck 'er!

What do
parrots eat?

Pollyfilla.

Which animal is a
really
good driver?

A steer!

What do
you call a crate
of ducks?

A box of quackers.

What do you get if you cross a duck with a firework?

A firequacker.

What is the difference between a maggot and a cockroach?

Cockroaches crunch more when you eat them.

Why was the insect kicked out of the park?

Because he was a litterbug!

What do you give a sick bird?

Tweetment!

Knock Knock!
Who's there?
Bet.
Bet who?
Bet you don't know whose knocking!

Knock Knock!
Who's there?
Spectre.
Spectre who?
Spectre Morse, you're under arrest!

Knock Knock!
Who's there?
Cologne.
Cologne who?
Cologne Ranger!

Knock Knock!
Who's there?
Gino.
Gino who?
Gino me? Open the door!

Knock Knock!
Who's there?
Chester.
Chester who?
Chester minute!

Knock Knock!
Who's there?
Adrian.
Adrian who?
Adrian my hair because it's wet!

Knock Knock!
Who's there?
Aldous.
Aldous who?
Aldous who want to leave the room, put your hand up!

Knock Knock!
Who's there?
Diana.
Diana who?
Diana-mals are restless, let them out the cage!

Knock Knock!
Who's there?
Gay.
Gay who?
Gay-topen, that's how the pigs got out!

Knock Knock!
Who's there?
Henrietta.
Henrietta who?
Henrietta hat because he lost a bet!

Knock Knock!
Who's there?
Bella.
Bella who?
Bella bottom trousers!

Knock Knock!
Who's there?
Fiona.
Fiona who?
Fiona of the house, I've come for rent!

Knock Knock!
Who's there?
Joe Namath.
Joe Namath who?
Joe Nameth not
on the door, that's
why I knocked!

Knock Knock!
Who's there?
Ivor.
Ivor who?
Ivor fortune!

Knock Knock!
Who's there?
Fiona.
Fiona who?
Fiona had something
better to do, I wouldn't
be hanging around here!

Knock Knock!
Who's there?
Sigrid.
Sigrid who?
Sigrid service –
open up!

How can you tell if you are looking at a police glow-worm?

It has a blue light!

Why are glow-worms good to carry in your bag?

They can lighten your load!

What do you get if you cross a glow-worm with a python?

A fifteen foot strip light that can strangle you to death!

When should you stop for a glow-worm?

When he has a red light!

What is the maggot army called?

The apple corps!

What is a worm's favourite band?

Mud!

What happened to the glow-worm who was squashed?

He was de-lighted!

What reads and lives in an apple?

A bookworm!

Knock Knock!
Who's there?
Martin.
Martin who?
Martin of peas won't open!

Knock Knock!
Who's there?
Phineas.
Phineas who?
Phineas thing happened to me on the way home!

Knock Knock!
Who's there?
Rosa.
Rosa who?
Rosa potatoes grow in our garden!

Knock Knock!
Who's there?
Celeste.
Celeste who?
Celeste time I lend you money!

Knock Knock!
Who's there?
Tamara.
Tamara who?
Tamara the world!

Knock Knock!
Who's there?
Eddie.
Eddie who?
Eddie body home?

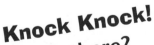

Knock Knock!
Who's there?
Zena.
Zena who?
Zena stealing my things!

Knock Knock!
Who's there?
Buster.
Buster who?
Buster town please!

270

What do you call an ant who lives with your great uncle?

Your great-ant.

What do you call an ant with frogs legs?

An ant-phibian.

Where are sheep and cattle sold?

At the stock market.

"Doctor, doctor, I feel like an electric eel!"

"That's shocking!"

Why did the jellyfish blush?

Because the sea-weed.

How do eels get around the sea?

They go by octobus.

What do you call a lion that's black and blue all over?

Bruce.

Why is the sky so high?

So birds don't bump their heads.

Knock Knock!
Who's there?
Juliet.
Juliet who?
Juliet the same amount but she's OK!

Knock Knock!
Who's there?
Sadie.
Sadie who?
Sadie end of the joke!

Knock Knock!
Who's there?
Euripedes.
Euripedes who?
Euripedes these trousers and you'll pay for a new pair!

Knock Knock!
Who's there?
Robin.
Robin who?
Robin the larder is wrong!

Knock Knock!
Who's there?
Shelly.
Shelly who?
**Shelly con carne –
Mexican food!**

Knock Knock!
Who's there?
Cyril.
Cyril who?
**Cyril pleasure to
meet you again!**

Knock Knock!
Who's there?
Morris.
Morris who?
**Morris in the pot,
help yourself!**

Knock Knock!
Who's there?
John.
John who?
John me for a cup of tea!

Knock Knock!
Who's there?
Toothy.
Toothy who?
Toothy is the day before Wednesday!

Knock Knock!
Who's there?
Drucilla.
Drucilla who?
Drucilla kid you! You might have got hurt!

Knock Knock!
Who's there?
Uriah.
Uriah who?
Keep Uriah on the ball!

Knock Knock!
Who's there?
Athol.
Athol who?
Athol'd my bike so now I have to walk everywhere!

Knock Knock!
Who's there?
Beth.
Beth who?
Beth wishes!

Knock Knock!
Who's there?
Ann.
Ann who?
Ann-onymous!

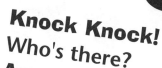

Knock Knock!
Who's there?
Chad.
Chad who?
**Chad to make your
acquaintance!**

Knock Knock!
Who's there?
Esme.
Esme who?
**Esme petticoat
hanging out the back?**

Knock Knock!
Who's there?
Noah.
Noah who?
Noah a good place to find more jokes?

Knock Knock!
Who's there?
Stefan.
Stefan who?
Stefan nonsense!

Knock Knock!
Who's there?
Della.
Della who?
Della-katessen!

Knock Knock!
Who's there?
Belinda.
Belinda who?
Belinda church steeple!

Knock Knock!
Who's there?
Evadne.
Evadne who?
Evadne new teeth through?

Knock Knock!
Who's there?
Dick.
Dick who?
Dick potatoes out of the ground!

Knock Knock!
Who's there?
Bill.
Bill who?
Bill-tup area!

Knock Knock!
Who's there?
Miss.
Miss who?
Miss L. Toe is nice at Christmas!

Knock Knock!
Who's there?
Census.
Census who?
**Census Saturday
we don't have to
go to school!**

Knock Knock!
Who's there?
Grammar.
Grammar who?
**Grammar is my
favourite relative!**

Knock Knock!
Who's there?
Disaster.
Disaster who?
**Disaster be my
lucky day!**

Knock Knock!
Who's there?
Nettie.
Nettie who?
**Nettie as a
fruitcake!**

Knock Knock!
Who's there?
Sal.
Sal who?
Sal-ong way to Tipperary!

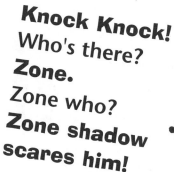

Knock Knock!
Who's there?
Zone.
Zone who?
Zone shadow scares him!

Knock Knock!
Who's there?
Miniature.
Miniature who?
Miniature open your mouth you put your foot in it!

Knock Knock!
Who's there?
Hannah.
Hannah who?
Hannah partridge in a pear tree!

Knock Knock!
Who's there?
Anna.
Anna who?
Anna-nother thing, how long do I have to wait for you to open up!

Knock Knock!
Who's there?
Tillie.
Tillie who?
Tillie comes home, I'll wait here!

Knock Knock!
Who's there?
Weasel.
Weasel who?
Weasel while you work!

Knock Knock!
Who's there?
Amahl.
Amahl who?
Amahl shook up!

Knock Knock!
Who's there?
Ina Clare.
Ina Clare who?
Ina Clare day you can see for miles!

Knock Knock!
Who's there?
Sis.
Sis who?
Sis anyway to treat a friend?!

Knock Knock!
Who's there?
Emmett.
Emmett who?
Emmett the back door, not the front!

Knock Knock!
Who's there?
Sultan.
Sultan who?
Sultan pepper!

Knock Knock!
Who's there?
Virtue.
Virtue who?
Virtue get your beautiful eyes from?

Knock Knock!
Who's there?
Honda.
Honda who?
Honda the tree!

Knock Knock!
Who's there?
Step father.
Step father who?
One step father and I'll be inside!

Knock Knock!
Who's there?
Formosa.
Formosa who?
Formosa the summer I went on holiday!

Knock Knock!
Who's there?
Pharoah.
Pharoah who?
Pharoah-nuff!

Knock Knock!
Who's there?
Geordie.
Geordie who?
Geordie-rectly to jail, do not pass go, do not collect £200.

Knock Knock!
Who's there?
Scold.
Scold who?
Scold outside!

Knock Knock!
Who's there?
Izzy.
Izzy who?
Izzy come, Izzy go!

Knock Knock!
Who's there?
Pizza.
Pizza who?
Pizza cake would be great right now!

Knock Knock!
Who's there?
Eamon.
Eamon who?
Eamon my way out. Do you want to come?

Knock Knock!
Who's there?
Cellar.
Cellar who?
Cellar? No I think it can be repaired!

Knock Knock!
Who's there?
Harriet.
Harriet who?
Harriet all my lunch!

Knock Knock!
Who's there?
Lauren.
Lauren who?
Lauren order!

Knock Knock!
Who's there?
Faye.
Faye who?
Faye Kearings!

Knock Knock!
Who's there?
House.
House who?
Hugh's fine thank you!

Knock Knock!
Who's there?
Delores.
Delores who?
Delores on the side of good people!

Knock Knock!
Who's there?
Barry.
Barry who?
**Barry the treasure
so no one will find it!**

Knock Knock!
Who's there?
Odette.
Odette who?
Odette's a bad sign!

Knock Knock!
Who's there?
Yelp.
Yelp who?
**Yelp me! My nose is
stuck to the window!**

Knock Knock!
Who's there?
Artichoke.
Artichoke who?
**Artichoke on
his food!**

Knock Knock!
Who's there?
Punch.
Punch who?
Not me please!

Knock Knock!
Who's there?
Statue.
Statue who?
Statue? This is me!

Knock Knock!
Who's there?
Stop-watch.
Stop-watch who?
Stop-watch you're doing right now!

Knock Knock!
Who's there?
Jaws.
Jaws who?
Jaws truly!

Knock Knock!
Who's there?
Roland.
Roland who?
Roland butter please!

Knock Knock!
Who's there?
Gilda.
Gilda who?
Gilda fly that won't leave me alone!

Knock Knock!
Who's there?
Alice.
Alice who?
Alice forgiven, come back!

Knock Knock!
Who's there?
Hope.
Hope who?
Hopefully that present is for me!

Knock Knock!
Who's there?
Carman.
Carman who?
Carman get it!

Knock Knock!
Who's there?
Santa.
Santa who?
Santa text reminding you I'd be here!

Knock Knock!
Who's there?
Nora.
Nora who?
Nora bone!

Knock Knock!
Who's there?
Argo.
Argo who?
Argo to the beach on holiday!

What is a polygon?

A dead parrot.

What kind of bird opens doors?

A key-wi.

What do you get if you cross an ant with half a pair of knickers?

A pant.

What do baby swans dance to?

Cygnet-ure-tunes.

What do you call
an old ant?

An antique.

What is a duck's
favourite TV show?

The feather
forecast.

Where do birds
invest their money?

In the
stork-market!

Where do blind
sparrows go for
treatment?

The Birds
Eye counter!

What happened when the owl lost his voice?

He didn't give a hoot!

What happens when ducks fly upside down?

They quack up.

What do you get if you cross an elephant with some locusts?

I'm not sure, but if they ever swarm, watch out.

What do you get if you cross a rabbit with an elephant?

Big holes in your garden.

What did the fish say when it swam into a wall?

"Dam!"

What do you get if you cross a woodpecker with a carrier-pigeon?

A bird who knocks before delivering its message.

What is smaller than an ant's dinner?

An ant's mouth.

Why did the elephant put his trunk across the path?

To trip up the ants.

Knock Knock!
Who's there?
Zeke.
Zeke who?
Zeke and ye shall find!

Knock Knock!
Who's there?
Guinevere.
Guinevere who?
Guinevere going to tell me?

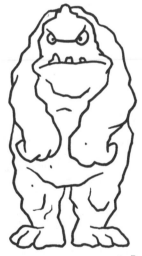

Knock Knock!
Who's there?
Don.
Don who?
Don just stand there, say something!

Knock Knock!
Who's there?
Sherry.
Sherry who?
Sherry dance?

Knock Knock!
Who's there?
Datsun.
Datsun who?
Datsun really old joke!

Knock Knock!
Who's there?
Bernadette.
Bernadette who?
Bernadette all my dinner again!

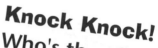

Knock Knock!
Who's there?
Egypt.
Egypt who?
Egypt my best china plate!

Knock Knock!
Who's there?
Noah.
Noah who?
Noah yes – which one is it?

Knock Knock!
Who's there?
Ella.
Ella who?
Ella mann-tree my dear Watson!

Knock Knock!
Who's there?
Ada.
Ada who?
First Ada Kit!

Knock Knock!
Who's there?
John.
John who?
John the Navy and see the world!

Knock Knock!
Who's there?
Owl.
Owl who?
Owl aboard!

Knock Knock!
Who's there?
Yacht.
Yacht who?
Yacht's up Doc?

Knock Knock!
Who's there?
Hal.
Hal who?
Hallo to you too!

Knock Knock!
Who's there?
Tucson.
Tucson who?
Tucson and two daughters are enough kids!

Knock Knock!
Who's there?
Pizza.
Pizza who?
Pizza pie please!

Knock Knock!
Who's there?
Stu.
Stu who?
Stu late to ask questions!

Knock Knock!
Who's there?
Mummy.
Mummy who?
Mummeasles are better so can I come in?

Knock Knock!
Who's there?
Louisana.
Louisana who?
Louisana boyfriend broke up!

Knock Knock!
Who's there?
Socket.
Socket who?
Socket to me!

Knock Knock!
Who's there?
Ooze.
Ooze who?
**Ooze been sleeping
in my bed?**

Knock Knock!
Who's there?
Sophie.
Sophie who?
**Sophie come to the
end of the lesson!**

Knock Knock!
Who's there?
Lilac.
Lilac who?
Lilac a trooper!

Knock Knock!
Who's there?
Atlas.
Atlas who?
Atlas we can talk properly!

What do you call a pig in a striped shirt and a mask?

A piggy bank robber.

What do you call a musical ladybird?

A hum bug.

What do you get if you cross an octopus with a skunk?

An octopong.

How do you start a jellyfish race?

Get Set!

What goes straight up in the air and wobbles?

A jellyfishcopter!

What happened to the dog that fell into a lens-grinding machine?

He made a spectacle of himself.

What happened when the shaggy dog swallowed a teaspoon?

He wasn't able to stir.

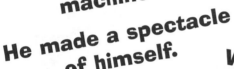

What has 2,000 eyes and 4,000 feet?

A thousand dogs.

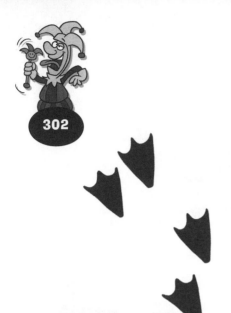

Knock Knock!
Who's there?
Dennis.
Dennis who?
Dennis say I need a filling!

Knock Knock!
Who's there?
Alaska.
Alaska who?
Alaska my mummy!

Knock Knock!
Who's there?
Moppet.
Moppet who?
Moppet up before it gets sticky!

Knock Knock!
Who's there?
Wotsit.
Wotsit who?
**Wotsit matter
to you?**

Knock Knock!
Who's there?
Costa.
Costa who?
Costa lot!

Knock Knock!
Who's there?
Halibut.
Halibut who?
**Halibut letting me in
on the secret?**

Knock Knock!
Who's there?
Jade.
Jade who?
Jade a whole cake today!

Knock Knock!
Who's there?
Ivan.
Ivan who?
Ivan no idea!

Knock Knock!
Who's there?
Paul Lee.
Paul Lee who?
**Feeling Paul-lee so
I stayed in bed!**

Knock Knock!
Who's there?
Water-skier.
Water-skier who?
Water-skier Dof?
It won't hurt you!

Knock Knock!
Who's there?
Athene.
Athene who?
Athene you about,
haven't I?

Knock Knock!
Who's there?
Dwayne.
Dwayne who?
Dwayne in Spain
falls mainly on
the plain!

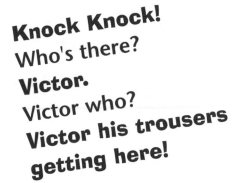

Knock Knock!
Who's there?
Victor.
Victor who?
Victor his trousers getting here!

Knock Knock!
Who's there?
Noise.
Noise who?
Noise to see you!

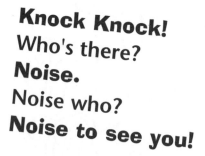

Knock Knock!
Who's there?
Senor.
Senor who?
**Senor mother out
and let me in!**

Knock Knock!
Who's there?
Vanessa.
Vanessa who?
**Vanessa you going
to grow up?**

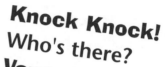

Knock Knock!
Who's there?
Enid.
Enid who?
Enid some food!

Knock Knock!
Who's there?
Worzel.
Worzel who?
It's upstairs on the left!

Knock Knock!
Who's there?
Marcella.
Marcella who?
Marcella's full of water!

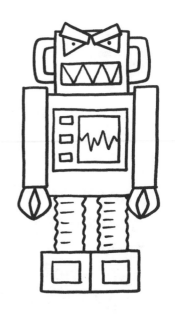

Knock Knock!
Who's there?
Juanita.
Juanita who?
Juanita 'nother hot dog!

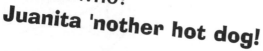

Knock Knock!
Who's there?
Harvey.
Harvey who?
Harvey gonna play this game forever?

Knock Knock!
Who's there?
Kansas.
Kansas who?
Kansas the best way to buy tuna!

Knock Knock!
Who's there?
Fajita.
Fajita who?
Fajita another thing I'm going to be sick!

Knock Knock!
Who's there?
Obi Wan.
Obi Wan who?
Obi Wan of the good guys, let me in!

Knock Knock!
Who's there?
Dad.
Dad who?
Dad fuel to the fire!

Knock Knock!
Who's there?
Paine.
Paine who?
Paine in the neck!

Knock Knock!
Who's there?
Kenneth.
Kenneth who?
Kenneth little kids play with you!

Knock Knock!
Who's there?
Havanna.
Havanna who?
Havanna a wonderful time – wish you were here!

Knock Knock!
Who's there?
Organ.
Organ who?
Organise a party, it's my birthday!

Knock Knock!
Who's there?
Dancer.
Dancer who?
Dancer is simple, it's me!

Knock Knock!
Who's there?
Pam.
Pam who?
Pam-per yourself!

Knock Knock!
Who's there?
Fanta.
Fanta who?
Fanta Claus!

Knock Knock!
Who's there?
Ohio.
Ohio who?
Ohio Silver!

Knock Knock!
Who's there?
Dawn.
Dawn who?
Dawn leave me out here in the cold!

Knock Knock!
Who's there?
Felipe.
Felipe who?
Felipe bath, I need a wash!

Knock Knock!
Who's there?
Doug.
Doug who?
Doug good deeds and you'll go to heaven!

Knock Knock!
Who's there?
Handel.
Handel who?
Handel with care!

Knock Knock!
Who's there?
Lock.
Lock who?
Lock who it is – after all this time!

Knock Knock!
Who's there?
Plane.
Plane who?
Plane innocent won't save you!

Knock Knock!
Who's there?
Orest.
Orest who?
Orest that man!

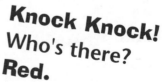

Knock Knock!
Who's there?
Red.
Red who?
Reddy, aim, fire!

Knock Knock!
Who's there?
Crush.
Crush who?
Crush on you!

Knock Knock!
Who's there?
Kitten.
Kitten who?
Kitten the park hit me with a ball!

Knock Knock!
Who's there?
Handsome.
Handsome who?
Handsome sweets through the door!

Which animals are the snootiest?

The ones that live in trees – they look down on all the other creatures.

What do you get if you cross a blind lion with a spiked shoe?

A very cross blind lion.

What did one flea say to the other after a night out?

"Shall we walk home or take a dog?"

Which elephants have the shortest legs?

The smallest ones!

What is a flea's favourite book?

The itch-hiker's guide to the galaxy!

Why did the stupid boy wear a polo neck sweater?

To hide his flea collar!

What is a bear's favourite drink?

Coca-Koala!

What is the difference between a dead bee and a sick gorilla?

One is a seedy beast and the other's a bee deceased.

How do you make an
elephant laugh?

Tickle its ivories.

How do you hire a
teddy bear?

Put him on stilts.

Why was the little
bear so spoiled?

Because its
mother panda'd to
its every whim.

What should you call
a bald teddy?

Fred bear.

What fish gets up the river at 100 mph?

A motor pike.

What is black and white and red all over?

A dalmatian with a bad sunburn.

What is taller when it sits down than when it stands up?

A dog.

What is a dog's favourite tree?

The dogwood.